SURFACE MODELLING BY COMPUTER

Proceedings of a Conference jointly sponsored by The Royal Institution of Chartered Surveyors and The Institution of Civil Engineers, and held in London on 6 October, 1976

The Institution of Civil Engineers
London, 1977

:::

Organizing committee

:::

D Taffs (Chairman)
H Cowling
P Dirdal
M Grist
J R Smith

Production editor: Thelma Darwent

ISBN: 0 7277 0029 4

Published and distributed by Thomas Telford Ltd for The Institution of Civil Engineers, 26-34 Old Street, London EC1V 9AD

Printed by Inprint of Luton (Designers and Printers) Ltd

Contents

Paper 1
::
Review of surface modelling
::

J P Stott, BSc(Eng) PhD MICE (Principal Scientific Officer, Transport and Road Research Laboratory, Crowthorne)

1.   A surface model is the mathematical representation of a surface in such a form that it can be used in design calculations.   The use of surface modelling in some branches of civil engineering has much increased in recent years.   The increase has paralleled the development of computers and computer programs which can make rapid calculations and process large amounts of data such as would be impracticable manually.   The purpose of this paper and conference is briefly to review the present state of surface modelling in civil engineering and to promote an exchange of experience between different users.

DIFFERENT USES OF SURFACE MODELLING.

2.   Several different uses of surface modelling in civil engineering are mentioned below to illustrate the variety of problem areas.   Some are considered in-depth in later papers to this conference.

3.   In the design of new roads and road junctions, digital ground models have been used extensively to describe the shape of the ground.   These models are an integral part of several suites of road design programs, for example the BIPS and MOSS systems (refs.1 and 2).   They are used in the design of earthworks, drainage and structures and in the calculation of land-take.   Optimization programs which require digital ground models as data input have been developed to minimize earthworks (ref.3).   Perspective drawings produced by the computer can replace hand-built models to show the shape of the ground as well as visibility distances along roads and aesthetic features of the design including the appearances of bridges (ref.4).   Similar facilities are being developed for the realignment and improvement of existing roads (ref.5).

4.   Digital ground models have been used for the design of railways in Australia and South America as well as for roads.

5.   Earthworks are important in designing airfields and the use of surface modelling has allowed optimization principles to be employed.   Modelling methods have been used in reshaping and strengthening existing runways (ref.6).   The new runway surface is defined mathematically and superimposed on the existing surface which is represented by a model.   The quantities of reshaping materials can be calculated from the superimposition, and the new runway surface changed by varying, within appropriate constraints, the parameters of the mathematical definition so as to minimize the cost of the work.

6.   The co-ordination of architecture and civil engineering is seen in the use of surface modelling in building design (ref.7).   Hand-made models to represent a building, completed and in its proper surroundings, can be replaced by perspective drawings, which conveniently display the consequences of variations in the design.   The location and co-ordination of services, stairwells, supporting walls, etc. is greatly facilitated in a large multi-storey building by modelling the flooring allocations.   Complicated networks of piping in processing plants can be designed and laid-out by modelling methods.   Surface modelling may be used to predict the earthwork quantities resulting from different positions of building foundations and adjacent roads, and the use of models and optimization principles to optimize building locations over a wide area has been proposed.

7.   Sub-surface modelling is used to define the distributions of soils in the ground and to construct data banks (ref.8).   The soils information is processed by computers to interpolate soil types between boreholes, etc.   Zones of difficult soils can be highlighted where more detailed survey is required.   Specialised maps of an area can be produced showing engineering properties of the soils, e.g. in terms of bearing strengths for foundations.   The recording of sub-surface data is included in a digital ground model for road design (ref.9).

8.   In coal-mining areas, computerised techniques are used to predict subsidence of the ground surface based on the geometry of the underground, worked strata (ref.10).   In open-cast mining, subsoil information from boreholes is put onto a rectangular-mesh digital model;   volumes of excavation are calculated from cross-sections;   computerised

methods are under development to optimize the operation of the drag-line and haul trucks.

9.   The capacity of a reservoir and the effect of the impounded waters on the countryside can be calculated from a surface model as an aid to selecting the best position for the construction of a dam.

10.   Co-tidal charts are available to predict the height of the sea-surface and therefore, taken together with the level of the sea-bed, the depth of water in the sea at various times and places (ref.11).   Such information has applications in designing harbour works and off-shore structures, and in planning the routes of large sea vessels such as oil-tankers.

11.   No consideration of surface modelling would be complete without mention of the current work on digitising the Ordnance Survey maps (ref.12).   This work, amongst other benefits, should give engineers low-cost access to much digitised topographical data.

USE OF DIGITAL GROUND MODELS IN BRITAIN

12.   Digital ground models for road design are a particular form of surface model and they are considered in more detail so as to illustrate the possibilities of other types of model.

13.   Such a model has two essential parts;   a pattern of data points of known horizontal co-ordinates and heights which represents the shape of the ground, and an interpolation procedure to get the height of any point of known horizontal co-ordinates;   it can be linked to a set of road design programs to use the interpolated information.

14.   Historically, the first digital ground model for road design was produced by the Massachusetts Institute of Technology, USA in 1957.   The model was based on ground cross-sections extended beyond the boundaries of the road and the horizontal alignment of the road could be varied with automatic calculation of the quantities of earthworks.   The same principle is still used in the form of terrain sections (ref.13).

15.   Since that time, many other digital ground models h been developed in Britain and throughout the world whic'

various patterns of data points and types of mathematical interpolation. Later models embody facilities to improve the interpolation, the variability of spacing of points within a grid, and the division of the digital ground model into blocks for more efficient treatment in the computer.

16. At the present time, two types of digital ground model are available in the BIPS 3 system (ref.1), namely:

    square grid model: the data points in the model are situated at the nodes of a square grid. This arrangement tends to convenient storage and retrieval in the computer and to the blending of different kinds of information, e.g. surface and sub-surface information can be stored at the same point.

    triangles model: the data points are stored at the corners of linked triangles which are so positioned as to represent the shape of the ground. The model was developed to be used mainly with land survey.

    In addition, a third model is at present under development for inclusion in BIPS 3, namely:

    string-lines model: this model is based on contours although strings of three-dimensional points can be added. It is well adapted to aerial survey methods. The string-line principle has been applied to a system of supporting programs covering many aspects of road design and transport planning.

    A string-line model is already available as part of the MOSS system (ref.2).

17. Other digital ground models have been developed by public authorities and consultants and the variety must surely be sufficient to cover all possible applications, and indeed is such as to cause occasional frustration as to which model to choose.

18. There is no "best buy" amongst these models as they are appropriate for different purposes and situations; also, each basic type is capable of development to meet any shortcomings in it compared with other models. ⋁The best model for a particular occasion will depend on the purpose for which it is required, the shape of the ground, the previous experience f the user, whether aerial or land survey is to be employed,

the extent of development of facilities in the particular
model, and the supporting local facilities such as available
design programs and computer hardware.

19. Digital ground models can be used at all stages of design.   At the start of a project, the design is most open to
alternatives and it is desirable to study several horizontal
alignments so as to arrive at the best.   To do this effectively, the area of interest may be covered by a digital ground
model; the corresponding ground profile can then be derived
automatically for each alternative horizontal alignment.   At
route selection and feasibility stage, the need is for a wide
area of cover but a low accuracy so that a large scale
representation may be used - say 1:10000 or even 1:25000.
As the design of the alignment progresses and more information
becomes available, it is common to make changes to the alignment and these can be made using a digital ground model without resurvey which would be costly and delay the project.
At final design stage, better accuracy is needed over a
narrower area and a scale of 1:2500 or even 1:500 is appropriate.

BENEFITS TO USERS OF SURFACE MODELS

20. The benefits to users of surface models are found
essentially in terms of improved design and covenience.   A
design can be made against a wider background of information.
More alternative approaches to a design can be studied and
compared leading to better and cheaper structures.   It is
not generally practicable to attribute a quantified saving to
the use of surface models but substantial savings have been
shown to be possible where they have been used together with
optimization methods.   Changes in a design can be made rapidly and without reacquiring data which may be costly and
delay the project.   After the data has been set-up for a
surface model, further processing by a computer is fast and
does not demand human resources so that staff effort is reduced.   The use of computer graphics as a form of surface
modelling provides a visual display and hence a better
appreciation of the design;   they may be used to give perspective drawings, displays on video units or, in appropriate
cases, as cine films.

COSTS TO USERS OF SURFACE MODELS

21. The costs to users of surface models are those of w
ing the computer programs, acquiring the data for the
and running the computer.   Computer programs are now

able for many models and, having been developed centrally for wide usage, are either free of charge or fairly cheap. The acquisition of large amounts of data over a wide area is necessarily costly. However, the size of the operation in many applications, e.g. road design, has encouraged some organisations to specialise in large-scale data acquisition and improved techniques have been evolved. In land modelling, air survey methods have been much used, perhaps because of the cheapness of surveying large numbers of points after the photogrammetric plates have been set-up (ref.14). Land surveyors are in the market at prices competitive with air survey (ref.15).

22. In consequence of improved methods, the creation of digital ground models is relatively cheap and, as an example, a model of 100 points per hectare over a road scheme length of 10 km. and width of 1 km. will cost around £20000; the same road will cost about £10M to build.

23. The cost of computer time varies according to the number of points in the model, their pattern of storage, the mathematical form of interpolation, the computer programs which process the data and the characteristics of the computer. Whilst it is not possible to quote particular examples, it appears that differences in computers, including their operating systems, and in the data-handling routines in computer programs can change the cost of running the same digital ground model by a factor up to 10 times.

ACCURACY OF SURFACE MODELS

24. Calculations based on surface models are liable to be in error from three causes:

   data acquisition (or survey) errors,

   modelling errors (due to interpolation between data points within the surface model),

   design errors (due to assumptions made in the design calculations).

25. Data acquisition and design errors are common to both modelling and conventional design processes. Modelling errors are discussed in a later paper (ref.16) and they have been studied elsewhere (ref.17). Interpolation or modelling errors can be reduced by having more data points so as to get a satisfactory accuracy in a surface model. The

relationship between accuracy and density of data points is important in specifying surface models.

ACKNOWLEDGEMENT

This Paper was prepared at the Transport and Road Research Laboratory and is published by permission of the Director.

REFERENCES

1. DEPARTMENT OF THE ENVIRONMENT, COUNTY SURVEYORS' SOCIETY. BIPS 3, British Integrated Program System for Highway Design. March 1975.

2. CRAINE G., HOULTON J. and MALCOLMSON E. MOSS Modelling Systems. MOSS Consortium (Durham, Northamptonshire and West Sussex County Councils), 1974.

3. STOTT J.P. The optimization of road layout by computer methods. Proc. Inst. Civ. Engrs., Part 2, 1973, 55, March, 67-85, discussion ibid., December, 963-968.

4. STOKES S. Graphics in ground modelling. Paper No. 8 to this Conference.

5. HIGHWAY ENGINEERING COMPUTER BRANCH. VALOR Suite of Road Realignment Programs. Department of the Environment, London, November 1972.

6. STICKLING R.W. A polynomical optimization technique for improving the vertical alignment of an existing airport runway. PTRC Summer Annual Meeting, 9-12 July, 1974, University of Warwick.

7. WHITTON D. Building industry applications. Paper No.7 to this Conference.

8. CRATCHLEY C.R. Engineering geology of South Essex. Paper No.6 to this Conference.

9. HIGHWAY ENGINEERING COMPUTER BRANCH. A draft FREEWAY User's Manual. Department of the Environment, London, 1973.

10. MARR J.E. The application of the zone area system to the prediction of mining subsidence. Paper No.457, Proc. Inst. Mining Engrs., October 1975, 53-62.

11. GLENN N.C.   Co-tidal charts and their uses.   Paper No.5 to this Conference.

12. HILL G.   The development of digital maps.   Ordnance Survey Professional Paper 23, Southampton, 1972.

13. WILLIAMS G.M.J.   Computers in highway design.   Surveyor, 14 September 1968, 42-48.

14. SCOTT L.   Data collection for DGM's using aerial survey methods.   Paper No.3 to this Conference.

15. HOWES L.A.   Data acquisition for DGM's by ground survey method.   Paper No.2 to this Conference.

16. GRIST M. and STOTT J.P.   Modelling errors in digital ground models.   Paper No.4 to this Conference.

17. HEATHERINGTON S. and CRAINE G.S.   Aerial surveyed string digital ground models.   PTRC Summer Annual Meeting, 9-12 July 1975, University of Warwick.

Data acquisition for digital ground models by ground survey methods :.:

L A Howes, BEM ARICS (Chief Surveyor, Engineering Surveys Ltd, West Byfleet)

1.   Land Surveyors have for centuries been engaged on the task of acquiring original data regarding the shape and disposition of the ground and supplying this information in the form most acceptable to the user.   In the past the visible output has usually been via the medium of drawn topographic plans, which are essentially surface models in graphic form.   Such plans have graphically portrayed the ground surface as it exists together with the features and detail upon it.   The usefulness of these plans to the user has depended upon their accuracy and therefore their reliability in defining the actual ground surface.   Large scale topographic plans for engineering projects have provided the basic building blocks in the form most convenient to engineers, designers and other users, who need only specify to the land surveyor either the use to which the data will be put or the form of the data and the tolerances that are required.

Until the advent of modern computer systems, users had to manually investigate these plans for their required purposes but now the possibilities are being realised of holding plan information in computer data banks for subsequent interrogation and analysis by purposes-written programs.   Survey data acquired in the field has always been in a digital form and is therefore immediately computer acceptable.   Ground height information in the form of three dimensional co-ordinates can be stored as a 'model' in the data bank, whilst 'detail' information, roads, buildings, boundaries etc., can be stored as two dimensional co-ordinates.   As yet, no one appears to have

Institution of Civil Engineers. Surface modelling by computer. ICE, London, 1977, 9-14

9

devised a satisfactory structure for digitised plan detail which would enable a 'detail' model to be stored and inter-rogated. There are however, numerous methods of stor-ing ground height information as 'ground' models and interrogating them. Such models are synonymously known as Digital Ground Models (D.G.M.s) or Digital Terrain Models (D.T.M.s).

SURVEY INSTRUMENTATION

2. The last decade or so has seen very rapid advances in the development of modern surveying instruments which have both increased the speed of acquisition and the accuracy of data obtained in the field by ground survey methods.

There is now available a large variety of E.D.M. equip-ment capable of measuring distances to accuracies of from a few centimetres to within one millimetre, and the time taken for each observation, over ranges up to 30 - 40 kilometres or more, can be measured in minutes. E.D.M equipment is now used almost exclusively for control net-works and detail acquisition, in conjunction with glass arc theodolites capable of being directly read to 1 second of arc and which incorporate automatic vertical indexing. This assists the rapid observation of the vertical angles needed to compute the height differences between points, so that corrections can be applied to the E.D.M. measured slope distances to reduce them to horizontal distances. Auto-matic levels are now available which, with in-built or attached micrometers, enable spot heights to be readily and consistently taken to a relative accuracy of a few millimetres. Continuing improvements and combinations of instruments led to the first automatic recording electronic tacheometer being introduced into the U.K. in 1973. This was the Zeiss Reg Elta 14, which was soon followed by a similar instrument, the Aga 700 recording tacheometer.

The Reg Elta 14 Tacheometer resembles a large theodolite, the telescope of which combines the trans-mitting and receiving optics for distance measurement,

together with the normal sighting optics.   The electro-
optical distance measurer uses phase comparison between
a reference signal and the signal reflected back from the
target prism.   The light source used is a luminescent
gallium-arsenide diode emitting directly modulated light
at near infra-red frequency, invisible to the human eye.
Each distance recorded is the mean of one thousand phase
measurements and results are unaffected by interruptions
of the light path.   The electronic components for distance
and angle measurements are housed in the two uprights
supporting the telescope.   Distances, horizontal and
vertical angles are read automatically and are recorded
onto punched paper tape, together with a manually set
12 digit register code which uniquely references the data.

The impact of these instruments on land surveying was
considerable for they enabled the observations to the actual
ground point being measured to be automatically recorded
in digitised computer readable form.   They can be
immediately accepted by the computer for processing and
subsequent storage and this has virtually eliminated the
error problems associated with the manual processes of
booking, transcribing and reducing field observations.
The speed of acquisition (approximately 30 seconds
measuring time per point) and the reliability and ease of
the observations has increased the facility of recording a
greater density of points, thus creating a more detailed and
more accurate model of the ground.

D.G.M.s AND THE LAND SURVEYOR

3.   As it is understood today a D.G.M. is essentially
height information in a computer acceptable form.   Such
information has always been collected by land surveyors
and has been manually used as the basis for contoured plans
and marine charts.

Since the shape of natural ground is random and of varying geometry, the D.G.M.s so formed from the original
field data will be non-geometric in structure but will
represent the ground as it exists.

The problem with any D.G.M. is that heights will be required for points at which no field measurement exists, so it becomes necessary to interpolate between the known height points.

The data stored in a D.G.M. will rarely be wanted in its stored form but information will need to be interpolated from it.   In order to simplify this interpolation the non-geometric D.G.M, obtained by direct ground survey methods, can be interrogated and ordered into a fine mesh D.G.M, the cell size of which is optimised from the density and distribution of the measured data.   We, at Engineering Surveys Ltd. , employ this method using cell sizes to the order of 5 metres or so.

The accuracy of the D.G.M. so derived depends largely on how adequately the true surface has been defined in the field.   In assessing the accuracy of any model, consideration must be given to the maximum permissible departures of a derived value from its true value and to the sign distribution of such departures since these will have a considerable effect on all calculations made using the model.

The land surveyor therefore needs to be aware that his depiction of the ground is as near representative as possible.   His natural feel for the ground should ensure that all salient heights are taken and that there is a sufficient density of points to adequately depict the surface. All points must be uniquely referenced and coded so that any non-representative points, e.g. ditch levels, can be screened out from the D.G.M.

Some users require various specific forms of geometrically structured D.G.M.s such as square, triangular or stringline. This really is to confuse the issue by mixing up the data on which the D.G.M. is derived with the model itself, in addition the constraints on the surveyor of following this geometric pattern are severe and of doubtful value. Even where the terrain is open and non-obstructed, the setting-out and levelling of

geometric patterns over large areas is time consuming and
negates the use of modern instrumentation and techniques.
Such data need to be observed in an ordered sequence
and the reconnaissance time required to identify
'stringlines' and 'triangles' in the field is often disadvantage-
ous and non-economic for the land surveyor. In practise
this data is often impractical to observe directly in the field.
Originally it was designed to be   digitised from the stereoscopic model derived from overlapping aerial photographs
in a photogrammetric plotter.

The aim of our operations as surveyors is to eliminate
error sources attributable to human activities as far as
possible by not putting undue constraints on the field
surveyor in the operation of his field work and by
mechanising as far as possible the office work entailed
in the survey.   It was because of our company assessment
of the weakness inherent in man driven plotting machines
that caused Engineering Surveys Limited to channel its
energies towards computer driven plotting machines, with
the computer handling the original field data.

CONCLUSION

4.   The automation of land surveys has now reached the
stage where all aspects of a survey can be integrated,
from the acquisition of data in the field, the reduction and
calculation of the data and the outputting of the final results
in the form required by the user, either in digital form,
printed listings or as graphic output.

Computer stored D.G.M.s are used by land surveyors
today as a part of the computer-automated processes
of contouring, section plotting, volume calculation and
route optimisation and the importance of using ground
survey methods as an effective, reliable and accurate
system of data capture for D.G.M.s are now being
recognised.

Modern instruments and computer facilities enable
ground models to be economically formed directly,
without the necessity of going through the drawing stage

and manually digitising models from the topographic plans.
By utilising modern developments ground surveys can be
made more reliable by reducing sources of human error,
resulting in a better quality product to the user. Land
surveyors can be left free to follow normal field practises
when surveying an area of ground and engineers can be
provided with an accurate surface model which can be
interrogated for their design purposes.

Recent trends in the survey requirements of engineers
and other users are for larger scales of plans and for
greater accuracy specifications. With land and
construction costs continually increasing, the cost benefit
of more and more detailed information is becoming more
apparent. The future would seem therefore to suggest a
growing demand for more accurate detailed data available
in computer usable form and modern ground survey
techniques will play a significant role in this sphere.

Data collection for digital ground models using aerial survey methods :

L Scott, FRICS (General Manager, Fairey Surveys Ltd, Maidenhead)

Historical background & introduction

1. Soon after the invention of photography, about 140 years ago, and long before the first successful heavier-than-air flying machine had evolved, a Frenchman demonstrated the use of vertical aerial photography for making maps, by using kites or balloons to suspend a camera above the ground. However, not until the end of World War II had technology advanced far enough to enable aerial photography to compete effectively with traditional methods for precise land sur- veying operations.

2. Probably, the most important considerations in the collection of DGM data using aerial survey are those affect- ing the flight planning and the photography. The organis- ation responsible for carrying out the operation must have properly equipped aircraft and highly specialised cameras, as well as skilled personnel.

Aerial survey cameras

3. There are many kinds of aerial cameras and other remote sensing devices in use today for different purposes, rang- ing from spy satellites to low-flying, high-speed aircraft. The cameras most used for aerial mapping applications are those with a wide-angle, single lens system of 152mm nominal focal length, which take photographs in a negative format measuring 230mm x 230mm. Such cameras cost in the region of £20,000, which at first sight seems to be astronomical, but when one considers the function that they are required to perform, this is not so, for the tolerances to which they work and their reliability in field conditions are quite re- markable. For example, the lenses have a resolving power in the order of 40 to 50 lines per millimetre at the focal plane; the displacement of image points in the focal plane

is less than 10 microns and the actual displacement pattern
is known by calibration to enable even these small distortions to be removed such that residual displacements of
image points from their true position in the focal plane are
within 1 or 2 microns; the film, which is 240mm wide, has
to be transported and flattened into the focal plane to an
accuracy of a few microns, all within a time of 3 seconds;
the shutter can be set for exposures as short as 1/1000th
second. Likewise, the films used in these high performance cameras have to be of a comparable standard: they
must be dimensionally stable and able to resolve detail to
a similar order to the camera lens. Fig. 1.

Fig. 1 Modern aerial survey camera installed in
aircraft, with operator.

Flying & photography

4. The aircraft which carries out the aerial survey flying
must be properly adapted and equipped to ensure that the
high precision of the camera system is preserved: the
camera port must be positioned correctly; navigation sights
must be provided; some degree of temperature and humidity
control is necessary; not least, it is vital to have an
experienced aircrew.

5. Every operation must be carefully prepared, good
flight planning being important, not only to ensure a
successful sortie but also to facilitate the rest of the
survey operation. Whilst modern air survey cameras will
produce acceptable photography in fairly poor weather, for
best results, optimum atmospheric conditions must be
sought. Ideal conditions, unfortunately, cannot be predicted with any accuracy from weather forecasts, as they
usually only last for an hour or two, in transient conditions between frontal systems. The experienced survey
pilot will be able to·exploit fully these opportunities.
(ref. 1 & 2)

6. One of the first considerations when flight planning
is to decide on the photograph scale. This usually
depends on the mapping scale and accuracy tolerances -
principally for heighting - that have been specified.
The scale of the photograph is a function of (i) the flying
height and (ii) the focal length of the camera. Since the
aerial cameras most commonly used for mapping purposes have
a nominal focal length of 152mm (6 inches·), the photograph
scale can be considered simply as a function of flying
height. It is usual to express photogrammetric heighting
accuracy as a fraction of the height from which the photography was taken. The root mean square error for measuring
spot heights is in the order of 1/5000th part of the flying
height. The spot-heighting accuracy specified for a project
will therefore indicate the minimum photo scale that is
required, e.g. if the heighting accuracy is not to exceed
$\pm$0.1 metres RMSE, then flying height must not exceed
500 metres which, with a 152mm focal length camera, gives
a minimum photo scale equal to 1/3,300 (ref. 3)

7. Aerial photography for the survey project has to be
flown in straight runs, photographs being taken such that
each frame overlaps the adjacent one by 60%, $\pm$5%.
Frequently, a long, narrow area, e.g. for a route survey,
can be covered in a single strip of photography, but in

cases where more than one run is needed, these are generally flown parallel to one another with a lateral overlap
of 25% $\pm$10%. (ref. 1 & 2) Fig. 2.

Ground control
=====

8. Ground control is required for all precise photogrammetric surveys. Frequently, points established for

Fig. 2 Diagram showing how overlapping photographic
cover is achieved during an aerial survey
flight.

other purposes are suitable, e.g. for a road project, permanent ground markers may have to be installed along the route and co-ordinated by field survey as part of the operation - these markers being used subsequently by the engineer for setting out the works. The markers can be installed and signalised before the sortie is flown, so that they will be clearly identifiable on the photography. Such a practice is especially helpful in rural areas, which are often lacking in the firm detail features necessary for obtaining fine, photo-point control. In cases where the layout of permanent ground markers does not give a broad enough control platform for the aerial survey, additional points - usually levels, only - are established after the sortie has been flown. Aerial triangulation, which is an analytical method of linking together the stereoscopic models covering a strip or a block, is frequently used in order to densify a ground control framework, thereby providing optimum control points on every overlap. (ref. 3)

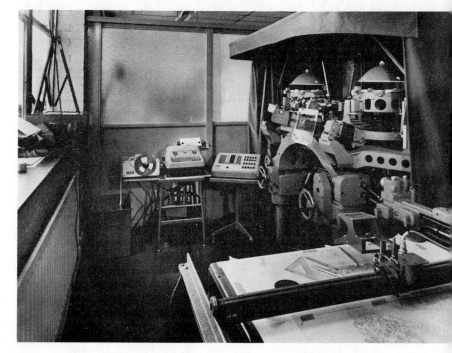

Fig. 3 Photogrammetric plotting instrument equipped with digitiser for automatic registration of co-ordinates.

Photogrammetry

9. Measurement of the DGM will be able to start when the photography and ground control are available. Usually precision plotters such as the Wild A8, Zeiss (East) Stereometrograph or the Zeiss (West) Planimat are employed, although other instruments, such as the Wild B8, Kern PG2 and Zeiss (West) Planicart, might be equally suitable for some DGM specifications. The instrument must be properly equipped with an automatic co-ordinate registration device. Fig. 3.

Fig. 4   Vertical aerial photograph taken over Oxford.
Note displacement of tops of buildings caused
by central perspective: the effect of these
distortions is completely removed during the
photogrammetric process.

10. Briefly, the photogrammetric process is the means by
which the perspective views of the two adjacent, overlapping
photographs are converted into an orthographic projection.
Fig. 4. The instruments used for this transformation are
operated manually by the photogrammetrist, who having properly oriented the pair of photographs, in the form of
glass or stable-film diapositives, can make measurements
and plot graphically from the three-dimensional image which
he sees, by means of a floating reference mark which can be
moved in three dimensions over and through the stereoscopic
model. The movements of the reference mark can be transmitted to a plotting stylus and a digital recorder.

11. Co-ordinates measured photogrammetrically are usually
recorded, initially, in a local cartesian system based on
the three axes of the plotting instrument. The known
control points are observed during the same operation,
so it is a straightforward matter to transform the data
into the desired ground values, e.g. National Grid planimetric co-ordinates and Ordnance Datum levels.

Form of digital ground models and methods of recording

12. Digital Ground Models (DGM's) comprise a schedule of
three-dimensional co-ordinates measured over an area of
interest. The pattern in which the points occur is a
method by which a DGM can be categorised, which can be
(i) Ordered (e.g. points in a square grid pattern) (ii)
Semi-ordered (e.g. points along section lines) or (iii)
Random. Aerial survey methods are suitable for collect-
ing DGM data in whatever pattern they have been planned
(ref. 4)

13. Ordered DGM points, e.g. at the intersections of
10m x 10m multiples of the National Grid, will occur
arbitrarily with respect to ground features. The method
of recording an ordered DGM photogrammetrically is for the
photogrammetrist to guide his floating mark to each
succeeding position by means of a stylus moving over a
control sheet, gridded in the terrestrial system and properly oriented on the drawing table of the instrument.
Having thus established the planimetric location of the
point, the operator then sets the reference mark onto the
surface of the model and, at the touch of a button, is able
to record the x, y, z co-ordinates before moving to the
next grid intersection. Fig. 5.

14. Semi-ordered DGM's can take the form of straight

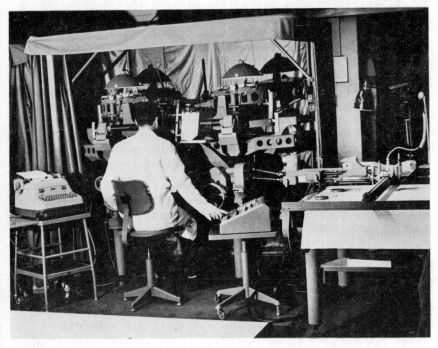

Fig. 5　Photogrammetrist measuring an ordered digital
　　　　ground model.

sections, points in strings along contour lines, or along
so-called characteristic terrain lines at significant
breaks of slope (as would occur at the toe of an embank-
ment, for example).　These DGM's can be observed and
measured in the same way as with ordered DGM's, that is
to say, by the operator making discrete pointings along
the lines in question.　However, modern registration
devices are capable of outputting sets of x, y, z
co-ordinates at pre-set intervals of distance or time:
thus, whilst the operator is following a contour on the
three-dimensional model, the DGM can be recorded automatically.

15. As stated earlier, the accuracy of photogrammetric
height measurement, expressed as RMSE minimum, is about
1/5000th part of the flying height.　Such accuracy is
ensured when vegetation is sufficiently low and herbac-
eous or of a shrubby, discontinuous character, to enable
the ground surface to be faithfully imaged on the photography.

Computer processing

16. Once the photogrammetric observations have been
completed, it is usually necessary for a certain amount
of computer processing to be applied before the DGM is
in a form suitable for the engineer. In the case of
square DGM's, the data have to be transformed to integer
planimetric values of the terrestrial grid, with the
elevations referred to the agreed datum. In the case of
string DGM's, the time or distance interval will have
been set to resolve the most intricate parts of the
ground; therefore, in the more regular areas there will
be far too many points recorded. Unnecessary points, in
such cases, are removed by means of an optimisation program, which fits a series of straight lines to the co-
ordinated points, rejecting any which fall within a set
tolerance to those lines. (ref. 5)

Cost of digital ground models by aerial survey

17. An idea of the cost of producing a DGM by aerial
survey methods is given in the following example:

DATE OF SURVEY: 1975 LOCATION: UK AREA: 1,000 hectares

DETAILS OF SURVEY: 1/1,000 scale mapping with 1 metre
                   V.I. contours; provision of perma-
                   nent ground markers; square DGM;
                   10m x 10m grid intersections -
                   approximately 110,000 points.

FLYING AND AERIAL PHOTOGRAPHY	£ 2,000
GROUND CONTROL & PERMANENT GROUND MARKERS	5,000
1/1000 SCALE MAPPING WITH 1M CONTOURS	15,000
PRODUCTION OF SQUARE DGM - 10m x 10m (ABOUT 110,000 POINTS)	6,000
TOTAL ..	£ 28,000

Conclusions

18. With the possible exception of DGM's covering
small areas and those which follow characteristic terrain
lines, some of which are not immediately recognisable on

vertical photography, aerial survey methods for DGM data
collection are generally more effective than ground
survey methods. Accessibility problems do not exist,
so that all points which define a DGM can be measured
directly, subject to their being clear of ground cover.
Measurement of the DGM can proceed, regardless of
weather and daylight conditions. However, it must not
be forgotten that the aerial survey method itself is
dependent on a successful flying and photographic operation at the outset.

REFERENCES

1. WOLF, P.R. Elements of photogrammetry. McGraw-
    Hill, New York, 1974, 562.

2. AMERICAN SOCIETY OF PHOTOGRAMMETRY. Manual of
    photogrammetry (third edition) George Banta Co.,
    Menasha, Wis., 1966, 1199, two volumes.

3. ROBINSON, G.S. Mapping from air photographs,
    part 2. The Surveying Technician, 1972, 2(4),
    December, 14-17.

4. GRIST, M.W. Digital ground models: an account
    of recent research. The Photogrammetric Record,
    1972, 7(40), October, 424-441.

5. CRAINE, G.S., HOULTON, J.M. & MALCOMSON, E. Moss -
    a modelling system for highway design and related
    disciplines. Public Works Congress, 1974, 15.

Paper 4

Modelling errors in digital ground models

M W Grist, BSc PhD (Photogrammetric Manager, Meridian Air
Maps Ltd, Lancing)
J P Stott, BSc(Eng) PhD MICE (Principal Scientific Officer,
Transport and Road Research Laboratory, Crowthorne)

1. A road designer needs to know the shape of the ground
surface so that he can fit the road alignment to it and
calculate the volumes of earthwork and the positions of toe-
lines - ie the lines along which the road side-slopes inter-
sect with the ground surface. He usually examines several
alternative horizontal and vertical alignments to get the
most' suitable and he modifies these alignments as the design
progresses. Digital ground models allow him to study
different alignments without resurvey, and they are widely
used in road design.

2. A digital ground model consists of a pattern of data
points of known horizontal coordinates and heights which
represent the shape of the ground, and an interpolation
procedure to get the height of any intermediate points of
known horizontal coordinates. A digital ground model is
usually operated in conjunction with road design computer
programs which use the interpolated information.

3. Several digital ground models are available with
different patterns of data points and associated interpolation procedures. There is a lack of knowledge as to what
densities of points to specify for different models and
types of ground.

4. The study outlined in this paper has been made to
relate modelling errors to densities of points for different
digital ground models and to advise on the best patterns of
points for different types of ground. It uses, as an
example, a test site at Worton in Wensleydale which was 1600
metres long by 100 metres wide.

ERRORS IN CALCULATING VOLUMES OF EARTHWORK AND POSITIONS OF
TOE-LINES

5. The calculation of volumes of earthwork and toe-line
positions is usually based on information about road and
ground cross-sections at intervals along the road. Each
ground cross-section is defined by several points along it
which are obtained from a digital ground model. Volumes of
earthwork are calculated by the end-area method* and positions of toe-lines from the intersections of road and
ground cross-sections.

6. Errors can occur at three stages in the calculation.

7. Survey errors arise in measuring the data points used
to make up the digital ground model; an overall assessment
of survey errors was made from the aerial photographic
measurements in the Wensleydale study and values are given
later in this paper.

8. Modelling errors occur during interpolation between the
data points within a digital ground model; they were the
main subject of the Wensleydale study.

9. Design errors are caused by assumptions made in the
design process; eg in calculating volumes of earthwork, the
areas between ground and road cross-sections are determined
at points along the road and they are then assumed to vary
linearly between these points, which is inaccurate. Design
errors have not been considered in the Wensleydale study.

10. All three of the above-mentioned categories of error
may be considered to include errors of three basic types,
each with its own characteristics: Random errors which
are small and equally likely to be positive or negative:
Systematic errors which also are small but with a bias in
the positive or negative direction; they are small errors
of the mean of a quantity over the complete length of a
section of road or ground: and gross errors which are
large, possible due to exceptional conditions or human
mistakes.

11. Although this study is concerned mainly with modelling

---

*The volume of a segment is assumed to be the average of
the areas of the ends multiplied by the length of the
segment.

errors, all the above errors need combining together to give a total error which may then be compared with an acceptable limit. Whilst there are no published acceptable limits, many designers consider that an error of 5 to 10 per cent of total volumes of earth work is reasonable, or 1 metre in the position of a toe-line.

THE WENSLEYDALE STUDY

12. The objective of the Wensleydale study was to determine the errors in the calculated volumes of earthwork and positions of toe-lines for different types of ground, using several different digital ground models to represent the ground surface with a range of densities of data points for each model.

13. The digital ground models included in the study were:

> square grid (BIPS) (ref 1): the data points are located at the nodes of a grid.

> terrain sections (TERRA) (ref 2): cross-sections are surveyed across the area of interest and perpendicular to the line of road.

> strings (MOSS) (refs 3 and 4): the ground is represented by data points located along strings and three variants of this model were investigated. In the first, the strings may represent contours - in this case, all data along a string have the same height and are stored in the form of two-dimensional points. The second is used for such ground features as sharp changes in slope or edges of rivers, etc - in this case the data in the string are stored as three-dimensional points. In the third variant additional data may be generated by a secondary interpolation process within the computer for those areas of ground where the strings are found to be too far apart for the simpler models to operate properly.

14. In addition to examining the five models listed above, a further test is in progress using a model in which the data is stored at the nodes of triangles. (The results of this work will be included in a more comprehensive report of the whole investigation in a later publication.)

TABLE 1

Characteristics of different types of ground in test site

Type of ground	Main characteristics of ground	Average width of road between toe-lines (m)	Average earthwork volume per 1 m length of road (m^3)
Flat	River valley no significant hillocks.	31	15
Uniform	Sloping plain, little undulation.	45	184
Undulating	Sloping, hillocks of glacial deposit, typically 10 m high, 50 m wide.	56	298
Rough	Sharply changing profile, 10 m high scarp and road in cutting.	59	418

15. All the above models use linear forms of interpolation in which the ground is assumed to be straight between adjacent data points.

16. A hypothetical road was designed on the test site as a basis for the study; it was 29.6 metres wide with 1 in 2 side-slopes.

17. The test site included zones of different types of ground and their main characteristics are summarised in Table 1.

18. The ground was surveyed by land and aerial methods. The land survey was made to provide a control framework for the air survey. The aerial photography was obtained at a scale of 1:3000. The main photogrammetric task was to prepare the input data for the various digital ground model systems and this was done with four different densities of data points for each model; these densities are shown in Table 2 in terms of number of survey points per hectare.

19. Each digital ground model operator processed the hypothetical road four times through his model using the different densities of points and produced ground cross-sections at 5 metre intervals. The information was put into road design programs and volumes of earthwork and positions of toe-lines were calculated at each cross-section.

20. Modelling errors were assessed separately for each digital ground model, density of points and zone of ground type. The basic procedure was similar for volumes of earthwork and for positions of toe-lines. At each cross-section, the value got from the highest density of points was regarded as temporarily "true" and the differences between it and the values for the other densities were regarded as errors attributable to the reduction in density. The values were not, however, absolutely "true" because errors of interpolation arise even at the highest density of points tested. Therefore, a further correction was made by linearly regressing the values for the different densities to intercept with the ordinate representing zero spacing, or infinite density, of points. This gave a set of errors of estimation at each cross-section and for each density of points within the models.

21. Errors in volumes of earthwork were treated according to two conventions in order to relate them as well as possible to the overall cost of earthworks. The activities in earthworks are cut, fill, haul, borrow and spoil. For the first treatment, it was appreciated that both cut and fill activities incur positive costs and therefore over-estimation of cut and over-estimation of fill were both treated as positive quantities. For the second treatment, it was appreciated that haul, borrow and spoil costs are determined by the earthworks mass-haul strategy and that this strategy is based on the out-of-balance curve which is obtained by subtracting fill from cut; for this reason, over-estimation of cut and under-estimation of fill were both treated as positive quantities. The two treatments have given similar results in general. The values in Table 2 were obtained using the first approach.

22. Errors in the positions of toe-lines were considered as positive if they over-estimated land-take.

RESULTS FROM THE WENDLEYDALE STUDY

23. Errors in volumes of earthwork and in positions of toe-lines were considered separately in the study.

Table 2 <u>Details of Results</u>

Digital Ground Model	Density of Model	Number of survey points per hectare				Combined proportiona errors in volumes of earthwork		
		Flat Ground	Uniform Ground	Undulating Ground	Rough Ground	Flat Ground	Uniform Ground	Undulatir Ground
SQUARE GRID	5m grid	441	441	441	441	0.096	0.015	0.010
	10m grid	121	121	121	121	0.098	0.015	0.013
	15m grid	58	58	58	58	0.093	0.019	0.012
	20m grid	36	36	36	36	0.145	0.021	0.020
TERRAIN SECTIONS	5m spacing	441	441	520	580	0.096	0.017	0.021
	10m spacing	121	121	180	253	0.112	0.022	0.026
	15m spacing	58	58	108	142	0.135	0.023	0.040
	20m spacing	36	36	66	92	0.167	0.032	0.052
STRINGS: CONTOURS ONLY	0.5m contour	210	310	993	1674	-	0.016	0.014
	1m contour	107	154	486	879	-	0.023	0.021
	1.5m contour	11	115	320	573	-	0.026	0.025
	2m contour	95	82	221	477	-	0.032	0.036
CONTOURS AND 3-D STRINGS	0.5m contour	272	310	1145	1952	0.087	0.016	0.028
	1m contour	169	154	637	1157	0.163	0.023	0.042
	1.5m contour	74	115	471	850	0.191	0.026	0.055
	2m contour	158	82	373	754	0.162	0.032	0.081
CONTOURS, 3-D STRINGS AND SECONDARY INTERPOLATION	0.5m contour	272	310	1145	1952	0.087	0.016	0.029
	1m contour	169	154	637	1157	0.163	0.023	0.033
	1.5m contour	74	115	471	850	0.191	0.026	0.044
	2m contour	158	82	373	754	0.162	0.032	0.078

Rough Ground	Combined random and systematic errors in positions of toe-lines (metres)				Gross errors in positions of toe-lines (metres)			
	Flat Ground	Uniform Ground	Undulating Ground	Rough Ground	Flat Ground	Uniform Ground	Undulating Ground	Rough Ground
0.061	0.13	-0.30	0.50	-1.71	0.46	-0.47	1.24	-4.80
0.076	-0.43	-0.26	1.08	-3.32	1.21	-	-	-
0.106	-0.47	-0.35	1.46	-5.31	1.23	-0.79	3.38	-12.80
0.187	0.63	-0.46	2.08	-6.17	2.13	-1.05	2.74	-11.20
0.059	-0.09	-0.45	0.86	-0.41	-	-	-2.14	-
0.073	-0.43	-0.68	1.59	-2.71	1.06	-	-3.91	-
0.128	-0.51	-0.77	2.43	-4.00	1.38	-	-	-8.09
0.182	-0.59	-0.95	3.30	-3.51	0.99	-	-8.18	-
0.033	-	0.59	1.58	0.54	-	-	-	-
0.083	-	1.01	3.05	5.96	-	-	-5.00	-16.71
0.119	-	1.66	4.42	6.76	-	-	-7.00	-18.17
0.137	-	2.20	6.20	6.16	-	-	-9.00	-16.71
0.021	-	0.59	1.04	-0.10	-	-	1.88	-1.0
0.020	-	1.01	2.20	0.61	-	-	4.88	-
0.035	-	1.66	3.09	0.49	-	-	6.73	-
0.053	-	2.20	4.26	0.42	-	-	8.64	-2.0
0.027	-	0.59	1.32	-0.10	-	-	3.88	-1.0
0.025	-	1.01	1.84	0.59	-	-	2.88	-
0.038	-	1.66	2.85	0.44	-	-	7.88	-
0.068	-	2.20	4.45	0.36	-	-	10.64	-2.0

Errors in volumes of earthwork

24. Errors in volumes of earthwork are important in so far
as they affect the total cost of earthworks. Therefore,
after errors had been determined at cross-sections as outlined above, they were summed to give a total error along
the length of road within each zone of ground type. These
total errors were then divided by the volume of earthwork
along the length of road so as to represent them as proportional errors, because acceptable limits of error are
usually expressed in this form.

25. The standard deviation of the random error in the total
volume of earthwork for the length of road on one type of
ground was calculated from the errors at each cross-section,
making the assumption that the distribution of errors as
measured on one occasion at several cross-sections was
representative of the distribution of errors for several
measurements at one cross-section. Then the standard
deviation of the random error in the total volume is:

$$\sigma_V = \sigma_{VCS}. \sqrt{N}$$

where: σ_V is the standard deviation of the random error in
the total volume of earthwork,

σ_{VCS} is the standard deviation of the random error in
the volume of earthwork at each cross-section,
and

N is the number of cross-sections.

26. The systematic error (mean of the error) for the length
of the road is similarly: $\bar{E} = \bar{E}_{VCS}. N$

where: $\bar{E}_V$ and $\bar{E}_{VCS}$ are the systematic errors of the total
volume and the volume at each cross-section respectively.

27. The survey errors mentioned earlier were found at
Wensleydale to have values for heights of individual points
as follows:

standard deviation of random error   0.04 metres
systematic error   0.03 metres

and these values were assumed to apply uniformly across the
site. They were converted from errors in height to errors
in volume by multiplying by appropriate areas, ie (width of
road between toe-lines) x (spacing between cross-sections).

28. The random and systematic errors due to both the modelling and survey processes have been used to estimate the size of the combined errors which will only be exceeded on 5 per cent of occasions. This combined error is given (with a confidence level of 95 per cent) by:

$$E = \bar{E}_{VM} + \bar{E}_{VS} + 2\sqrt{\sigma_{VM}^2 + \sigma_{VS}^2}$$

where E is the total combined error, $\bar{E}_{VM}$ and $\bar{E}_{VS}$ are the systematic errors due to modelling and survey respectively, and σ_{VM} and σ_{VS} are the random errors due to modelling and survey.

29. The results for the combined errors are shown in Table 2. They are shown as proportional errors and represent the total errors divided by the volumes as in Table 1. Also, the random proportional errors are a function of the length of road and they have been adjusted for a length of 1000 metres.

30. Gross errors were defined as having a value greater than 3.(standard deviation of random error) + (systematic error), and very few were found amongst errors in volumes of earthwork.

Errors in positions of toe-lines

31. Errors in positions of toe-lines may cause errors in land-take which result in difficulties in compulsory purchase procedures, especially if the requirement for land is under-estimated and supplementary orders become necessary. Because such difficulties are usually local, the errors were considered only in relation to individual cross-sections and they were not cumulated along the road as were errors in volumes of earthwork.

32. It was not possible to relate errors in positions of toe-lines to survey errors in the Wensleydale study.

33. The random and systematic errors have been combined using the relation: (combined error) = 2.(standard deviation of random error) + (systematic error).

34. The combined error was not, of course, measured in the study but it is a probable error which should not be exceeded in 95 per cent of situations according to the analysis.

35. The results are shown in Table 2.

36. Gross errors were defined as having a value greater than 3.(standard deviation of random error) + (systematic error), and many such errors were observed in different models, densities of points and types of ground. The number of these gross errors suggests that local factors make the distribution of errors in positions of toe-lines fairly non-Gaussian; it is known that large errors can occur when the road and ground side-slopes lie close together. The values of gross errors are shown in Table 2.

CONCLUSIONS FROM THE WENSLEYDALE STUDY

37. The following conclusions are presented from the study:

(a) the densities of model data required to limit errors in volumes of earthwork to acceptable values, for example to 10 per cent of the total volumes, can be deduced from the values in Table 2. These values relate to the Wensleydale study conditions and to a road length of 1000 metres but are thought to be reasonable for general use.

(b) the densities of model data required to limit errors in positions of toe-lines to acceptable values, for example to 1 metre, can also be deduced from Table 2.

(c) the criteria for errors in toe-line positions appear, in many instances, to be more demanding than for errors in volumes of earthwork.

(d) in general, the errors behaved consistently in that the magnitudes of error decreased as the densities of model data increased. However, there were several anomolous situations which indicated the mathematical complexity of the problem.

(e) in general, square grid and terrain section models have performed reasonably well in flat, uniform and undulating ground and less well in rough ground; string models have performed less well in flat ground due to the sparsity of contour lines (thus, it has not been possible to calculate toe-line positions) and well in rough ground. In general, the more complex models gave relatively small improvements of performance over the simpler models.

(f) the models required a wide range of densities of points, from 36 to 1952 per hectare. String models generated more points especially in the undulating and rough ground where the contours were naturally spaced more closely together. However, it must be pointed out that the method of obtaining data points varied with different models and that the relative cost of using a particular model does not necessarily depend on the number of points required.

(g) despite the different relationships between errors and densities of points, all the models produced closely similar estimates of the volumes of earthwork when used with the highest density of points.

ACKNOWLEDGEMENTS

The work described in this paper forms part of the programme of the Transport and Road Research Laboratory, and the paper is published by permission of the Director.

REFERENCES

1. DEPARTMENT OF THE ENVIRONMENT, COUNTY SURVEYORS' SOCIETY. BIP 3, British Integrated Program System for Highway Design, March 1975.

2. WILLIAMS G M J. Computers in highway design, Surveyor, 14 September 1968, 42-48.

3. CRAINE G, HOULTON J and MALCOLMSON E. MOSS Modelling Systems, MOSS Consortium (Durham, Northamptonshire and West Sussex County Councils), 1974.

4. HEATHERINGTON S and CRAINE G S. Aerial surveyed string digital ground models. PTRC Summer Annual Meeting, 9-12 July 1974, University of Warwick.

Paper 5
::
Co-tidal charts and their uses
::

Commander N C Glen, RN(retd) (Superintendent of Tidal Branch, Hydrographic Department, Ministry of Defence, Taunton)

1. Co-Tidal Charts show the vertical tidal movement of the sea in a diagrammetric form. Tides are caused by the gravitational attraction of the Sun and Moon on the seas of the Earth. The detailed movements caused are complicated for two basic reasons. Firstly, the orbits of the earth around the sun, and more importantly, the moon around the earth are not circular or even very regular. Secondly, the induced movements of the seas are very largely dependent on the natural frequencies of oscillation of the various oceans. These frequencies are governed by the dimensions of the water masses concerned which are also complicated with many obvious local variations. When the periods of the gravitational forces are the same, or nearly the same, as the natural frequencies of the seas, resonance will occur and the tidal movements be greatly amplified.

TIDAL THEORY

2. The basic period of the gravitational forces is two cycles per day. This is because the tide raising forces are not those acting directly on the earth by either the sun or moon, but the difference between the forces acting on the body of the earth and those acting upon the masses of water at the surface of the earth. Thus it is the forces relative to the earth which will cause the seas to move. As the gravitational forces are all inversely proportional to the square of the distance between the point of action on the earth and the sun and moon, it will be seen that these differences referred to above occur at the points of the earth nearest to, and furthest from the moon or sun. With the earth rotating once per day there will be two maxima of the tide raising force in each lunar or solar day. In fact it is the horizontal component of the tide raising

force which causes the water to move but the effect is to
cause a bulge of water centred about the line joining the
earth and the sun or moon. The two cycles of this semi-
diurnal tide raising force will only be the same if the
sun or moon is directly over the equator. If either is
north or south of the equator, which frequently occurs,
there will be inequalities in the two maxima in a day. This
effect which is called diurnal inequality and can most
easily be described mathematically by considering the
introduction of the additional frequencies of approximately
one cycle per solar or lunar day. A more detailed
description of these effects can be found in the article on
Tides in the Encyclopaedia Britannica (ref 7).

3.   The fact that all these movements are taking place on
the surface of a spinning globe has an effect due to the
Coriolos Force involved. This tends to cause the hori-
zontally moving water to run towards the equator. This
results in rotating systems of tides about nodal points
which are sometimes called Amphidromic Points. In addition
the frictional effects of the shallow waters on the
continental shelfs introduces marked variations in the
shapes of the tidal curves. These are usually described
mathematically by the use of higher harmonies and compound
constituents.

4.   Thus it can be seen that the water movements involved
are bound to be highly complicated. In order to enable
tidal predictions to be made observed variations in sea
level are analysed into a large number of simple harmonic
constituents. Each of these is referred to a known astronomical parameter in the orbits of the moon and the earth,
or in the case of the compound constituents, combinations
of two or more of these parameters. These constituents
will therefore have basic periods of about one, two, four
six or more cycles per day. Other periods are also introduced in some cases where additional accuracy is needed,
or the tide is particularly difficult.

CO-TIDAL CHARTS

5.   Each constituent is described by two constants, H the
amplitude and 'g' the phase lag between the astronomical
condition and the observed tidal movement. In order to
make satisfactory predictions it is normal to use as many
as 60 constituents which can be obtained from one year's

observation of hourly heights of the tide. For some very
complicated ports even more are required. However for the
purpose of Co-Tidal Charts it is usual to restrict the drawing to the four largest of these. Two are normally taken
to represent the diurnal variations and two semi-
diurnal variations, one in each series for the solar effect
and one for the lunar. The Hydrographic Department is about
to publish an Atlas for these four constituents, known as
K1, O1, M2 and S2, for the Persian Gulf. (ref 8). This
area has been specially chosen as one of considerable shipping and oil-tanker importance and where the diurnal and
semi-diurnal regimes are both very important and markedly
different from each other.

6.   In some parts of the world the diurnal inequality is
either so small or the changes in it are so slight that it
can generally be ignored without seriously affecting the
results obtainable from a co-tidal chart. One such area is
the continental shelf around the British Isles and the
North Sea. In these areas it is also usual to find that the
difference between the lunar and solar semi-diurnal regimes
are very small so that one chart can be used to describe
the tide as a whole. The chart which does this is published by the Hydrographic Department as Chart No 5058.
(ref 1). There are also two other charts of parts of the
southern North Sea which give greater detail in areas of
particular shipping importance and also one of the Malacca
Straits which are of great importance in the passage of
large oil tankers from the Persian Gulf to the Far East.
(refs 2, 3 and 6). These charts do not therefore represent
single harmonic constants but a combination of the semi-
diurnal constituents. The parameters used are Mean Spring
Range, which is equivalent to amplitude, and Mean High Water
Interval, which is equivalent to phase lag. The meaning of
MSR is obvious but MHWI is defined as the time interval
between the transit of the moon at Greenwich and the next
High Water. These parameters can either be obtained from
the harmonic constants or, preferably, by a non-harmonic
analysis of the observed data.

7.   The actual preparation and analysis of the data before
plotting is usually carried out by electronic computer. In
the Hydrographic Department programs have been written for
various forms of analysis. One of these is based on the
method published in Admiralty Tidal Handbook No 1 which
uses as its input 30 days' hourly observations of the
height of the tide. (ref 4). Longer periods of data are

usually analysed by programs developed by the Institute of
Oceanographic Sciences, Bidston. Some authors have developed methods for the analysis for shorter period of data,
one of these is published in Admiralty Tidal Handbook No 3,
but in general the constants obtained are seldom of sufficient accuracy to enable reliable charts to be drawn.
(ref 5). These methods can, however, be useful in cases
where it is required fill in detail in areas where the
general characteristics are already known. The Hydrographic
Department concentrates its efforts on obtaining at least
30 days' data to ensure reliable results.

8.   The drawing of the chart is carried out by plotting the
value of the parameters to be used on an outline map for every
station where they are available. These are usually sites
close inshore and thus an enclosed basin is much more satisfactory for a chart of this kind than an open coast where the
offshore ends of the contour lines are usually based on
little real data and the orientation of the lines become more a
matter of artistic judgement than of scientific fact. Where
offshore data is available from structures such as light
towers or oil rigs, this is always incorporated but
experience has shown that this data is seldom of the same
standard of accuracy as that obtained ashore.

9.   Attempts have been made to draw the co-tidal or contour
lines by computerised methods but these have seldom met with
much success. This is due to the generally low standard of
accuracy of the available data caused by the large meteorological effects which cannot be excluded from the observed
data. The final drawing is usually made by hand taking into
account certain obvious restraints. The lines all represent
the movement, in one way or another, of very large masses of
sea water and therefore sharp corners or sudden bunching
together of the lines are most unlikely. The general shapes
of the contours can usually be predicted from hydraulic considerations and theoretical tidal calculations.

10.   In all this work account must be taken of the close
relation between the amplitude and phase lag of a constituent, a fact which often seems to be missed. These
parameters may well be considered as vectors to the extent
that, if the amplitude of a vector is small its phase, or
in this case phase-lag has much less importance than if the
amplitude is large. This consideration must also apply to
the accuracy of the data obtained by analysis. Constituents
with small amplitudes may well have large inaccuracies in the

value of 'g' obtained. This obviously becomes important when
drawing the 'g' contours of small constituents. In fact if a
constituent is very small throughout the area it may not be
possible to draw a chart at all. There is thus a limitation
imposed on the preparation of the charts in that they can only
be drawn for those constituents with reasonable amplitudes
and hence well defined phase lags.

USES OF CO-TIDAL CHARTS

11.   Having obtained a co-tidal chart, or series of charts,
for the area these provide data from which it is possible to
assess tidal conditions for positions where actual observations
cannot be obtained. This is frequently the case when considering input for a mathematical model of the tides of a sea area.
The input will naturally be improved, in just the same way as
the chart would be improved, if some observational data can be
obtained near the limits of the model area. When inserting
new data on a chart account must be taken of the way in which
the new fits in with the old; when discrepancies are found,
as is often the case, the reliability of all the data in that
locality must be assessed in order to decide how best to improve
the chart. The output from a mathematical model can also be
compared with a suitable chart in order to detect if there are
serious errors in the modelling. From what has been written
regarding the production of these charts it must be apparent
that highly accurate agreement in every detail cannot be
expected. However there are many areas where data obtained
from such a chart, which has been carefully compiled, is likely
to be more generally representative than data from an individual series of observations.

12.   The charts are also used by mariners to obtain tidal
predictions for offshore areas not normally included in
Tide Tables. The areas of greatest importance are those,
often many miles from land, where the depths are so shallow
that large ships such as super-tankers must allow for the
height of tide if they are to cross in safety to reach their
destination. Equally the charts are used by Hydrographic
Surveyors when adjusting their soundings in the area so as to
ensure that they are correctly reduced to chart datum.

13.   Co-Tidal Charts can therefore be considered as one method
of intelligent interpolation of tidal data. Extrapolation from
these charts must carry the same dangers as any other form of
prophesy or hydromancy.

REFERENCES

1.   Chart No 5058, British Isles and adjacent waters, co-tidal and co-range lines. Hydrographic Department. Edition No 2   1974.

2.   Chart No 5059, Southern North Sea, co-tidal and co-range chart. 1971. Hydrographic Department.

3.   Chart No 5057, Dungeness to Hoek van Holland, co-tidal and co-range chart. 1974. Hydrographic Department.

4.   Admiralty Tidal Handbook No 1.   (NP 122(1)) The Admiralty Semigraphic Method of Harmonic Tidal Analysis. 1958. Hydrographic Department.

5.   Admiralty Tidal Handbook No 3.   NP 122(3) Harmonic Tidal Analysis (Short Periods) 1964. Hydrographic Department.

6.   Chart No 5084, Malacca Straits, co-tidal and co-range chart. 1973. Hydrographic Department.

7.   Encyclopaedia Britannica. 1971. Vol. 21.

8.   Chart No 5081. Persian Gulf, co-tidal atlas.   In preparation. Hydrographic Department.

Paper 6

:·

Engineering geology of south Essex

:·

C R Cratchley, BSc(Eng) MSc (Head of Engineering Geology Unit, Institute of Geological Sciences, London)

INTRODUCTION AND OBJECTIVES

1.   The geological and geotechnical survey of a large part of South Essex, bounded on the north by the River Crouch, on the South by the River Thames, and on the west by the 576 grid line, extended eastwards to cover Foulness Island and the offshore area investigated by others in connection with the projected Third London Airport site on the Maplin Sands. The work was commissioned by the Department of the Environment in order that geological criteria could be applied in the planning of urban development and access routes in the hinterland of the proposed Maplin airport.

2.   The main objectives were outlined at the outset of the survey as follows:

"..... This (environmental geological survey) should comprise primary geological investigation, engineering geology mapping and mineral assessment. It should provide a preliminary assessment of the ground conditions, related to geology, and a guide both to the allocation of suitable land to particular development needs and to the best forms of investigation and most economical forms of testing when further detailed site investigation is necessary."

OUTLINE OF THE WORK

3.   Work on an integrated study of the geology, engineering geology and sand and gravel resources started in September 1972, and the major part of the work was completed by August 1975. This work comprised geological survey by the East Anglia and South East England Field Unit, geotechnical investigation into the characteristics and disposition of the materials in the area by the Engineering Geology Unit, and sand and gravel

assessment by the Mineral Assessment Unit of IGS. The field
work included surface mapping, borehole, trench and penetrometer
investigations and geophysical surveys. Materials encountered
in excavation were described in an agreed uniform manner which
took into account characteristics likely to have a bearing on
engineering behaviour. These characteristics could also be
coded in a form suitable for computer storage. Examples of
these characteristics are: particle size estimates; degree of
weathering; stiffness (of clays), etc. Samples were also
collected for laboratory testing and analysis, and a fairly
comprehensive range of geotechnical properties was determined
together with mineralogy and micropalaeontology. The results
from many external site investigation reports were also
utilised in building up a comprehensive set of three-dimensional geological and geotechnical data.

DATA BANKING

4.   At the outset in collaboration with the Computer Unit
of IGS it was decided to establish a computer data bank of
geological and geotechnical information for the South Essex
area. The reasons for doing this were:

(a)   Data recording, in order to be machine readable,
        would have to be in an agreed, defined, uniform
        manner. This has advantages in attempting to
        describe geological materials.

(b)   The data bank would enable enquiries about ground
        conditions within the area to be answered rapidly,
        albeit in a generalised way.

(c)   The facility to produce contour plots, sections,
        borehole logs, etc., by computer graphic techniques
        would enable a large number of experimental maps,
        sections, etc., to be drawn rapidly during inter-
        pretation stages.

(d)   Statistical analysis, particularly multi-variate
        cluster analysis, could be used much more readily
        with a computer data bank than otherwise.

(e)   It was thought that updating of the information
        with subsequent investigation data would be easier
        with a computer system, and the necessary amend-
        ments to maps and sections could be done auto-
        matically.

OUTLINE OF COMPUTER DATA BANK

5.   Data collection and recording was carried out by field
geologists, information later being transcribed to coding
sheets by scientists and clerical officers. During trans-
cription, the geologist encoded a lithological description,
using single-character codes to indicate lithology, texture,
fissuring, etc. A fixed format was adopted because of its
simplicity for Fortran programming and because some punched
card processing would have been possible.

6.   The data management system was under the control of the
G-Exec system (ref. 1).

7.   Checking and correcting data proved to be a major task
with several cycles of validation being necessary to ensure
a virtually error-free bank. This process proved to be time-
consuming not only because of the detailed pattern of the
recorded information, but also because the stratigraphical
code, normally allocated by a geologist on site, might be
changed at a later date when further information led to a
change in the stratigraphical identification.

      Checks on quantitative geotechnical data were also made,
for example, to ensure that values of particular properties
fell within expected limits.

8.   Data storage on disc was arranged in nine data files as
follows:

      (a)   Borehole reference information, including
             borehole number, national grid co-ordinates,
             date of drilling, contractor, etc. (1089 records).

      (b)   Water level data.

      (c)   Lithostratigraphic information, including detailed
             lithological and engineering geological descriptions
             depths and identified stratigraphical subdivisions
             in each borehole (8740 records).

      (d)   Reference data on samples tested in the laboratory,
             including sample number and tests performed (3261
             records).

      (e)   Lithological descriptions of each sample in file
             (d) (2328 records).

(f)   Geotechnical test data for samples analysed
        (2751 records).

(g)   Additional geotechnical test data (375 records).

(h)   Grading information (1115 records).

(i)   Geotechnical consolidation data (192 records).

Cross-referencing between files was provided by index
files using the borehole reference number and sample number.

9.   Retrieval of data was performed by the G-EXEC system,
either from one file, e.g. a borehole log in English on the
line printer or from several files. For multivariate analysis,
information from several files had to be combined into one
larger file before retrieval took place.

10.   Display of data required either further processing on the
IBM computer or the punching of cards for processing on the
IBM 1130 or Univac 1108 computer. Display programmes most
frequently used with data on the 1130 were: contour maps,
borehole location plots, fence diagrams (graphic borehole
sections) and range charts (ranges of material characteristics
in a borehole). On the Univac 1108 and Calcomp plotter trend
surface maps, contour maps, graphic borehole logs, cross-sections,
isopachyte maps and perspective views were produced via the
sophisticated SACM (surface approximation and contouring
package).

THE GEOLOGICAL MODEL OF SOUTH ESSEX

11.   For planning and civil engineering development, one is
concerned with two principal aspects of the geology - classification of the materials into units of similar characteristics,
and mapping of the three-dimensional disposition of these units.
Furthermore, it is implied that the engineering characteristics
of each unit mapped can be used to give a general forecast of
probable engineering behaviour for planning purposes. Classification of the materials is frequently on the basis of
lithostratigraphy, i.e. geological deposits are broadly grouped
according to the manner and order of deposition and similarity
of lithology. These may or may not correspond with units of
like engineering behaviour, and in addition to the traditional
stratigraphical groupings of the geologist, geotechnical or
engineering geological groupings were also attempted in South
Essex. This was done mainly on the basis of observed lithology

and geotechnical properties, classification being carried out
by visual examination of borehole records. In addition cluster
analysis of a range of geotechnical properties held on the data
bank was carried out and this analysis confirmed the classification based on essentially lithological and observed
geotechnical characteristics. The present paper is mainly
concerned with the three-dimensional mapping of these units.

12. The geology of South Essex can be approximately summarised
for shallow engineering purposes, as a gently undulating surface
of firm to stiff, fissured silty clay (London Clay), continuously
covered by extensive flat-lying alluvial deposits in the east
of the area, and discontinuously by the remnants of other transported superficial deposits in the west of the area. These
deposits are discontinuous and variable and consist of sand
and gravel terraces left either by old rivers or by glacial
processes, deposits of loessic "Brickearth", silts and clayey
silts, probably wind blown, river alluvium deposited by present
day rivers, buried channel infill consisting of sand, gravel,
silt and clay in sequential layers, and sandy-silty and clayey
"head" resulting from down slope wash. These superficial
deposits are generally of the order of a few metres thick and
their variable and discontinuous nature makes them unsuitable
for computer mapping, with the exception of the Brickearth,
which is illustrated by computer graphic section and, within
its own outcrop, by contours of physical properties. This
deposit exhibits "metastability" in parts of its area of
outcrop and the mapping of this zone is important for found-
ation purposes.

13. The extensive alluvial deposits in the east of the area
reach more than 30 metres in thickness in places and can be
subdivided into five main lithological/geotechnical units -
a basal gravel, two soft silty clay units, an intermediate
level gravel, sporadically distributed, and an upper silty sand.
As the soft silty clay units are highly compressible, while
the gravels form good foundations for piles, the relative
depths and extents of these various alluvial subdivisions are
important. Computer sections and contour plots of both surfaces
and thicknesses have been produced, although significant
difficulties with programming were experienced, particularly
where repetition of units occurred in vertical sequence.

14. The London Clay surface itself is a relatively simple
surface to model by computer as there is a fairly large number
of boreholes which have penetrated superficial deposits to
London Clay, and it has some areas of outcrop in the west of the

area. The surface is gently undulating and dissected, the
result of erosion by rivers falling to a low sea level during
Pleistocene time. The SACM package produces a reasonably good
surface approximation consistent with the data points. Certain
errors are introduced, however, because of the way in which
the surface is computed. These errors apply also to the
alluvium sub-unit surfaces described in Para 13 above.

PRELIMINARY ASSESSMENT OF COMPUTER MODELS OF GEOLOGICAL SURFACES

15. The London Clay surface is an example of a continuous
geological surface which occasionally coincides with the ground
surface but is normally buried beneath other geological deposits.
X, Y, Z co-ordinates for points on the surface, retrieved from
the main data bank, are kept in a separate file and used to
generate a set of Z (depths or O.D.) values, at intersections
of a grid by SACM. The size of the grid is variable and there
is an optimum grid size depending on the spacing of the data
points. Apart from errors introduced in the basic data anom-
alous features which arise in the computer contouring process
include (a) the unsatisfactory portrayal of sudden steps or
faults in the surface, (b) the generation of apparently false
closures (both highs and lows) of amplitudes which are not
possible, or at least unlikely, on geological evidence (c)
false extrapolation of contours outside the geographical limits
of the data set.

These problems are compounded where multiple surfaces are
concerned, as with the subdivisions of alluvium in South Essex.
An "optional extra" in the SACM package enables the introduction
of a step or fault feature on the contour plot. Unfortunately
this was not available for use with the South Essex results.
Error (b) arises because of a steep gradient in the surface
recorded in two closely spaced boreholes when the other boreholes in the vicinity show approximately equal levels for the
surface. It can be controlled by putting maximum and minimum
limits on the level which the surface can attain. In South
Essex, such limits were applied to the grid values generated
by SACM. False extrapolation at the boundaries of the data
set can be restricted by limiting the contouring to a line
joining the outermost data points. The larger the data set,
the better the computed contour plot. However, the comparison
between hand drawn and computer drawn contour plots of the
London Clay surface suggests that there will continue to be
significant differences between a mathematical surface generated by computer and a "geological" surface drawn by a

geologist. Inevitably, the latter includes a large element
of interpretation or assumption about the form of the surface,
e.g. buried river valley or ice-generated feature. Possibly
the way ahead lies in some interactive process in which the
geologist can introduce certain types of feature (step-like
faults, lensing deposits etc) so as to modify the purely
mathematical surface generated by the computer. Undoubtedly,
the most satisfactory scientific solution is to have the
necessary number of data points in order to define the surface
accurately. In practical, economic terms, this is, unlikely to
be achieved, nor could it be justified.

CONCLUSIONS

16. The elaborate data bank established for the geological
and geotechnical data of South Essex has fulfilled most of the
objectives set for it; however, research is required into more
efficient and economical methods of data recording, data management and methods of automatic contouring, possibly involving
interactive processes.

17. The type of complex data bank established for South
Essex is probably not justified for the recording of available site investigation data in this country; a computer index
system would suffice.

ACKNOWLEDGEMENTS

18. I am indebted to the many colleagues in IGS who contrib-
uted to this project. The multi-disciplinary team included
members of the following Units and Departments: East Anglia
and South-east England Field Unit, Mineral Assessment Unit,
Computer Unit, Petrographical Department, Palaeontological
Department and Engineering Geology Unit. The Experimental
Cartography Unit advised and contributed in the use of the
SACM package.

This paper is published with the permission of the
Director of the Institute of Geological Sciences and the
Department of the Environment. The work was commissioned by
the Third London Airport Directorate of the Department of the
Environment and completed under contract DGR 482/17.

REFERENCE

1. Jeffery, K.G., Gill, E.M., Henley, S. and Cubitt, J.M.
   1975, G-Exec User's Manual. Atlas Computer Laboratory.

:.:

Building industry surface modelling applications
:.:

D Whitton, MSc ARICS (Ove Arup and Partners, London)

1.   The designer of an object in the built environment has two principal classes of problem.   In one class is the need for an accurate representation of the appearance of the finished object, be it building or bridge, showing both the relative size of the new construction in the environment within which it is to be positioned (Fig.1) and simultaneously bringing out the effect of surface textures and colour.   The other class of problem is in the detail of the construction, identifying the relative position of member and fixing, service pipe and floor finish.

2.   Present methods of achieving a representation of relative impact usually need the construction of physical models in timber or similar material.   These may vary from simple block representation which is suitable where the requirement is one of a check on the relative massing of various buildings or the impact of a new development on an existing landscape to a highly detailed scale representation.   The highly detailed model can also be used to plan service layouts in large or complex plant rooms or in process plant design where pipe routing can become almost impossible to represent by any other means.   The drawback of this solid material representation is that model building is slow and expensive and to be effective needs highly skilled workers.   Further, having reached a solution, any variation to judge the effect of alternative proposals is also an expensive problem.   Some of these difficulties have been overcome by the adoption of special model constructing kits similar to children's building brick sets.   These are useful advances but still require the final stage of transfer of information from model to information for the manufacturing team in the form of drawings.

3.   Many attempts have been and are being made to overcome the problem of iterative work with the associated model rebuilding and the interface between models and drawings using

Fig.1   Model of the relative size of a new construction to
        its environment

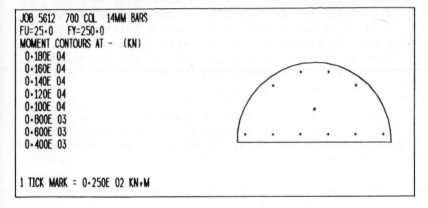

```
JOB 5612   700 COL   14MM BARS
FU=25·0   FY=250·0
MOMENT CONTOURS AT -   (KN)
 0·180E 04
 0·160E 04
 0·140E 04
 0·120E 04
 0·100E 04
 0·800E 03
 0·600E 03
 0·400E 03

1 TICK MARK = 0·250E 02 KN,M
```

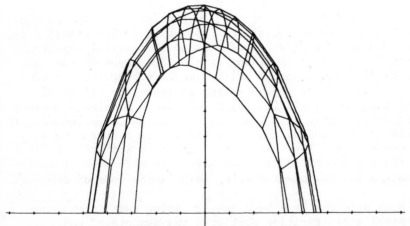

Fig.2   'Shell' of bending moments

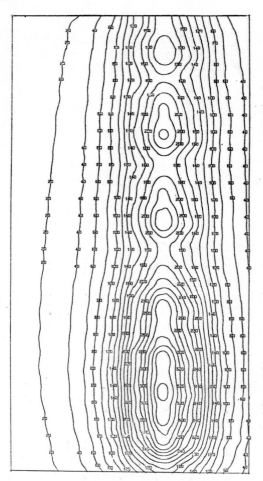

Fig.3 Light values at surface level from several artificial
       light sources

computer systems. The outline which follows is not exhaus-
tive but identifies some of the more general systems available. The systems are described from the user's viewpoint
and little reference is made to the efficiency of usage or
data storage.

4. The designer has two principal fields in which surface
modelling can be utilized. This may be either as a design
aid in, for example, plotting the behaviour of an item under
certain conditions or as a draughting tool in providing the
final design drawings.

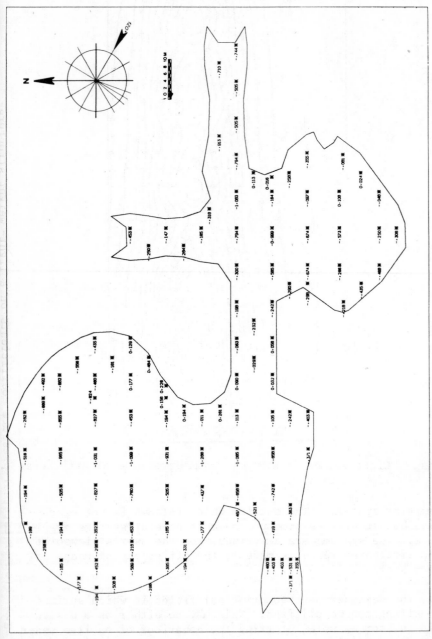

Fig.4 Plot of external pressure coefficients on a light-weight structure

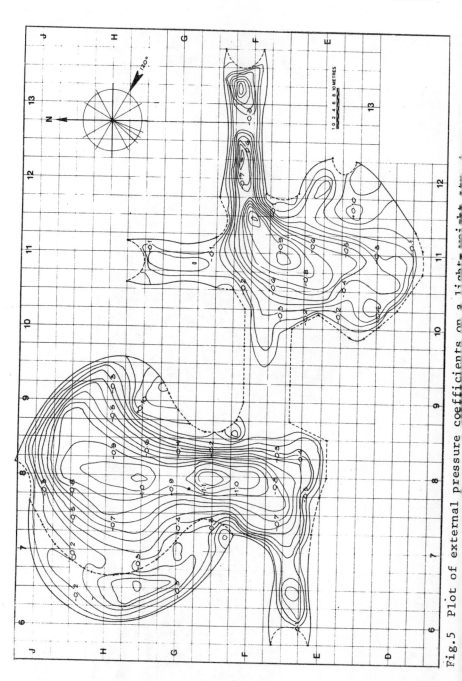

Fig.5   Plot of external pressure coefficients on a lightweight structure

Fig.6 Actual structure modelled in Figs 4 and 5

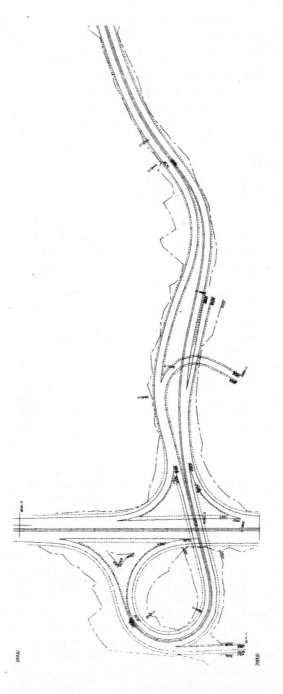

Fig.7 Intersection of two highways

5.   In the first category we have many examples, such as the
maximum bending moment of a column of varying cross-section
under different loads producing a 'shell' of limiting values
(Fig.2), a contour plot of reflected light values from a
series of specified light sources (in this case in a car
parking area (Fig.3)) or the plot of external pressure coefficients on a lightweight structure (Figs 4 and 5).

6.   All of these examples are generated in a form to give
the designer a picture of the forces at play in the problem
defined. While regular co-ordinate values could be easily
printed out, the designer's relationship with the problem,
the intimate 'feel' for the forces, is more easily conveyed
by the model when the real thing is not available (Fig.6).

7.   Turning to the design realization drawings those applications showing the greatest programming similarity to the
examples just described are the various ground contouring
packages. Used for either road or individual site representation there are many examples of satisfactory 'cut and fill'
optimisation programs available. Working from a regular pattern of level co-ordinates the road line can be plotted, services within the road run plotted and cross-sections presented. This work has now been carried on to cover housing
estate layout but is essentially two-dimensional in nature,
being the recording of events on one surface.

8.   The extension of this type of program to cover the common three-dimensional types of problem such as grade separa-
ted junctions is now well advanced. Highway design lends
itself well to the application of computers and the resulting benefits in speed of design and quality of product are
widely appreciated. Having established the ground model,
changes to the design can be accommodated with ease as in the
case of determining an optimum intersection of two highways
(Fig.7).

9.   Looking at the site before moving into the building itself we have the representation of the surface and the services crossing the site both above and below. Definition of
the ground surface and subsoil conditions can be represented
as for road works with infinite width. In large industrial
sites the many service runs to be planned need careful consideration. Some services can be considered as unidimension-
al links between two points but others have to be specified
as three-dimensional bodies. This can apply especially to
cables with high voltages or carrying high speed data where

the positioning of other services within a 'prohibited zone' can cause interference. Cabled services can often be defined relative to the ground surface model as far as depth goes but piped services, especially where gravitational forces are required for operation, have to move via a series of nodes. These nodes are defined in turn by definition of maximum and minimum depth below the surface required on grounds of economy, protection from frost and traffic and angle of pipe to the horizontal. Crossings of services, especially different types of service, have to be dealt with by hand and the plot recalculated.

10. The modelling of subsoil conditions is a powerful tool in the field of geotechnical studies. Using properties of symmetry the soil around a sheet pile wall can be analysed for seepage, given varying positions and sizes of well (Figs 8 and 9).

11. In building one has a three-dimensional problem which consists simultaneously of many overlays. If in a multi-storey building one takes as an example an intermediate floor/ceiling sandwich as might be found in an air-conditioned office building, the major horizontal three-dimensional items to define would be the structural floor, the suspended ceiling below and the service void between containing various service runs. While from floor to floor there are structural features giving repetition such as stairwells, columns and service shafts, many of the other items - surface finishes to floors and ceilings, duct sizes, light fitting and air extract types, to give a few examples - may all vary depending on the requirement of the building occupant. Adding on, in the simplest case, a roof and a ground floor slab to achieve a complete building, one has built up a system of layers of data defining the position of physical surfaces.

12. Lastly, moving away from the nuts and bolts of the building to the aesthetic views of the completed structure, the architect is interested not only in the finished shape but the surface textures which the materials will give. The 'grey scales' developed at Cambridge will help considerably and will no doubt be overtaken by present work there on a colour display. The massing of the parts of a large development or the effect of a new development within an existing area can be studied by rapid rotation of a displayed model and the work of the University of Strathclyde is useful here. At present the use of both of these techniques is limited by

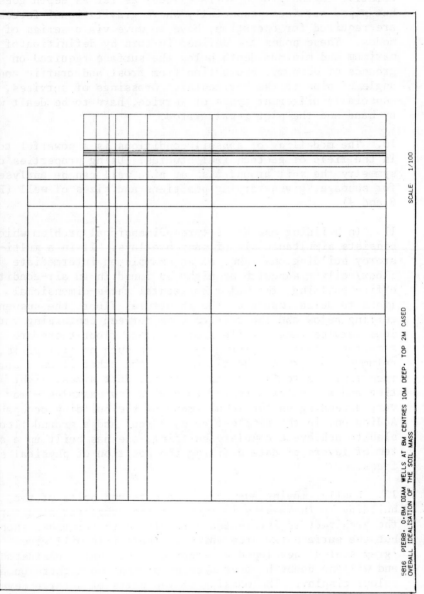

5B16 PIERB. 0·8M DIAM WELLS AT 8M CENTRES 10M DEEP. TOP 2M CASED
OVERALL IDEALISATION OF THE SOIL MASS

SCALE. 1/100

Fig.8   Section through basement showing well point

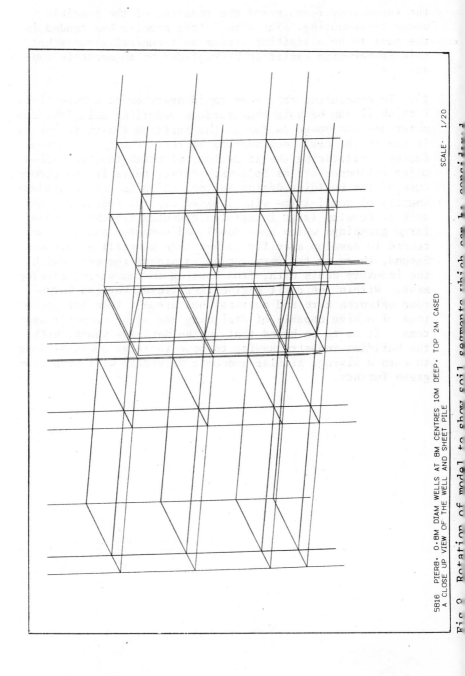

5816 PIER8· 0·8M DIAM WELLS AT 8M CENTRES 10M DEEP· TOP 2M CASED
A CLOSE UP VIEW OF THE WELL AND SHEET PILE   SCALE· 1/20

Fig 2 Rotation of model to show soil segments which can be considered

the input requirements and the reaction of the possible
users to computing. The size of the problem has tended in
the past to be a limiting factor on technical grounds but
this is becoming easier to be replaced by an economic con-
straint.

13. In concluding this very rapid overview of a huge field
I think it can be said that surface modelling using the computer has not moved as far in the building design sector as
it has in the civil engineering sector. There are various
factors influencing the situation, of which the two with a
major influence are as follows. First, there is the structure of the building design sector, which is formed predom-
inantly of small firms with limited capital resources, un-
able to develop large integrated computer systems. Those
large groupings which have developed computer systems have
tended to develop specific rather than generalized systems.
Second, there is the very varied nature of the work which
the industry deals with, from housing to industrial development. Within the civil engineering field, work on large
road networks here and overseas has brought together groupings of a size capable of designing and using computer systems. It is to be hoped that in the next few years, with
the building industry having to move to large overseas jobs
to earn a living, similar economic necessity will push progress further.

Paper 8

:::

Graphics in ground modelling

:::

S Stokes, BA (Applications Engineer, Computer Aided Design
Centre, Cambridge)

1. This paper discusses the current use of computers to
visualise surface models, where a surface model may represent structures of any kind as well as ground topography.

2. The capability of the computer to produce accurate perspective wire-line drawings has been used considerably in
the field of data presentation for some time. It was dis-
covered that as the amount of information contained in the
drawing increased, the resulting picture became very confusing and difficult to decipher (Fig. 1). The solution to
this problem was to remove the lines in the picture which
were hidden by faces of the object, and computer algorithms
have been available for some years to perform this function
(Fig. 2). The resulting program produces perspective views
of any object which can be described as a collection of
faces and edges, and removes the hidden lines from the picture (or optionally draws them dotted or in full), and can
produce this output on any device capable of displaying vectors (for example - storage tubes, drum plotters, flatbed
plotters, and also laser-scan devices).

3. Another method of representation involves the use of
raster-scan displays of some type of software which can remove the hidden surfaces in a perspective view, to produce
very realistic photograph-like effects. The display may consist of shades of grey to produce black-and-white effects,
although recent advances in hardware have made full colour
pictures possible, displayed on a standard colour television
monitor.

4. The two techniques described above form the basis for a
very large percentage of computer-produced perspectives.
The two programs take identical input data, in the form of a
list of points and planes defining the model.

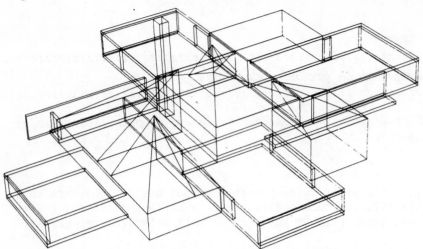

Fig.1. An example of a three-dimensional model drawn in perspective with no hidden-line removal

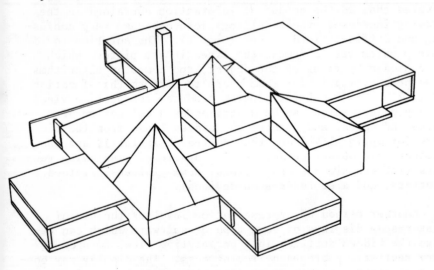

Fig. 2 As Fig. 1, with hidden-lines removed

5.   The use of these programs gives considerable flexibility
to the production of perspectives for any purpose - due mainly to the fact that, once the object has been defined as
above, the programs can produce views from any position
quickly and cheaply when compared to the equivalent manual
process (when it exists). The other main benefit of using

computers in this way is accuracy – this can be of great importance in some applications such as photomontage. The use
of the hidden-lines program to produce a geometrically exact
drawing which can be superimposed on a photograph and re-
touched by an artist has been found to yield extremely useful and informative results. It is also possible to combine
a series of views to produce a film.

6.   To date the main applications of this type of software
have been in the field of data-checking (e.g., finite element data, visibility through or round a collection of buildings, etc.), but as the output becomes more and more realistic with advances in software and the complexity of the
model which may be described, it seems that these visualisa-
tions may play an important part in assessing visual impact
and aesthetic appeal. There is reason to believe that the
experience gained in applying these techniques in the realms
of building and highway construction may be relevant to the
modelling of terrains. For the purposes of the rest of the
paper, a surface model may be taken to comprise any collection of surfaces or structures making up a particular site;
e.g., GTM for road design, geological features, bridges and
buildings, roads etc.

7.   A summary of the main features of hardware relevant to
computer visualisation follows.

COMPUTERS

8.   The basic choice is between remote access timeshared computers (bureaux), large computers 'inhouse' (which may never-
theless be somewhat remote from the engineering user), and
local mini computers (a growing trend).

Bureau computers

9.   This is the choice requiring lowest investment but providing least flexibility. The user is restricted generally
to a choice of teletype terminals, keyboard input, visual
display units (both of alpha-numeric and graphical) or remote job entry terminals. Often bureaux do not provide suitable graphics software or the peripherals required.

General purpose inhouse computers

10. The inhouse machine takes on a variety of aspects to the
CAD user depending on its size. The large installations
tend to be operated as inhouse bureaux, although not always

having the same range of software available as the commer-
cial bureau. This is a disadvantage which may be offset by
the greater access the user has to the computer management
for purposes of attaching special equipment and mounting
special software.

Mini computers

11. The term mini computer must be qualified. At one end
of the range are the small processors used as programmable
controllers for items of equipment; e.g., displays, plotters
or remote entry terminals. In the extreme case the processor will be pre-programmed and the user buys a 'black box',
or else a small range of functions may be open to modification by the user. At the other end of the range the mini
computer becomes a general purpose computer in its own
right, albeit usually aimed at a specific sector of the market by virtue of the software provided.

12. There is a trend towards the use of mini computers as
an inhouse computing facility. The capabilities and size of
the mini computers are growing, and in speed and efficiency
they now compete with the large general purpose bureau computers.

PERIPHERALS

I Low intelligence devices

13. By low intelligence we mean devices which do no processing of the input or output data, other than code or decode
the data transmitted, the data normally being transmitted as
alpha-numeric characters. The familiar teletype, the simple
storage tube terminal and many plotters fall in this category.

Teletype

14. The teletype terminal, operating at 15 or 30 characters
per second is an essential piece of CAD hardware. It is
used as an input/output terminal, controlling a user's interactive programs or in association with graphical equipment
in more comprehensive work station configurations.

Plotters

15. A tremendous variety of plotters are available, ranging
from fairly small low resolution drum plotters to very large,
accurate and fast flatbed plotters. With each plotter there

is usually associated a controller, or range of controllers, to allow it to be driven off time; this saves valuable computer time, as the computer is not held up by the relatively slow speed of the plotter. The type of plotter required in given circumstances has to be evaluated taking into account the required turn-around time, average complexity of drawings, and accuracy required.

Visual displays

16. The Tektronix storage tube is a visual display device which forms the basis of several manufacturers' terminals including Tektronix' own range of terminals. These provide a combination of keyboard and display screen, with x,y controls moving 'cross wires' displayed on the screen for picking off coordinates. The electronics provided for some terminals give extra facilities such as long vectors, arc drawing and varieties of character.

17. These terminals have no local processing power. The image is held permanently on the screen until erased, so that normally the whole screen must be cleared in order to modify a single feature. For many applications this is not a severe restriction and, where it is, the terminals are operated close-coupled to a computer and the problem overcome by using a high data transmission rate.

18. A variety of other devices may be connected in parallel with the Tektronix terminals, including a teletype, a hard copy unit which will reproduce the contents of the screen at any time, a cassette tape recorder, useful for recording and playing back demonstrations, and a graphics tablet, of which more later. This type of terminal is widely used for its cost-effectiveness both as a terminal in its own right and as a monitor for input and output through digitisers and plotters.

II Intelligent terminals

19. Intelligent terminals have some computing power and can carry out some processing functions independently from the main computer. This class of equipment could be taken to include plotters with sophisticated controllers, and visual displays with refresh graphics and advanced picture manipulation functions.

20. The range of intelligent terminals may be extended to include devices starting to become available, such as the

colour monitor and associated hardware mentioned earlier. This device gives the facility of being able to address individually every point on the screen, and to set its colour components to the desired value, this making possible a very wide range of applications.

21. Plotter controllers convert coded input data into incremental move instructions for the plotter drives. By including a programmable mini computer in the controller the amount of coded data which has to be supplied can be reduced, allowing complex drawing functions to be optimised and carried out with less data. This in turn allows plotters to be operated over communications lines. For remote plotting, data compression is most important and error checking is also necessary.

Interactive visual displays

22. There is a wide range of visual display configuration based on mini computers. The basic terminal consists of a visual display with light pen and/or keyboard and a graphics processor. The vector-drawing display operates in response to a list of display instructions in the processor, generally known as a display file. The instructions are executed repeatedly so that the displayed picture is refreshed and, by changing some instructions, parts of the picture can be modified.

23. This arrangement allows the use of a light pen as an interactive input device and also provides for selective erasure or modification of parts of the picture. The computer which runs the graphics processor may also be pre-programmed to carry out advanced graphical functions, such as scaling and rotation of views, and the same computer may be utilised to process the user's data in various ways. Alternatively (and more usually) the terminal is used in conjunction with a separate mini computer and memory.

Data input devices

24. Given some local computing power a wide variety of input devices may be used. Information to be input falls into three categories:

      (a) numerical data - quantities, dimensions;
      (b) graphical data - position, shape;
      (c) control data   - commands to control the computer
                                  programs and flow of data.

25. The choice of device depends on the type and quantity of data and on the ergonomic requirements. Combinations of devices are often used. They may be classified essentially into keyboard devices and coordinate reading devices, with various forms of technology invoked to produce the effect. Keyboards are convenient for numerical input in smallish quantities and for control commands; coordinate readers – digitisers and graphic tablets – are useful for graphical data and for control data, using the technique of a pre-programmed 'menu' affixed to the board. The light pen is a form of coordinate reader.

26. The electro-mechanical digitiser and the solid state graphics tablet are used in a variety of modes, including the combination digitiser/plotter (see below). Graphics tablets have tended to be low resolution devices (0.005 in to 0.025 in) and are lower in cost. Low resolution is adequate for many purposes including command input by menu or by character recognition. High resolution (0.001 in) is necessary in taking off maps and road drawings, especially at small scale, but in most engineering applications dimensional information is input separately in association with the digitised positional information.

III Interactive design systems

27. Combinations of input/output equipment with a mini computer, and various kinds of secondary data storage are now marketed together with operating software providing comprehensive drawing and command facilities.

SOFTWARE

28. Although there is a very wide range of hardware available to aid in the production of computer visualisation, this is not the case as far as software is concerned, particularly in the area of data generation. The software required falls naturally into two categories: 'input' software, which should give the user the ability to input data in the form which is most convenient to him (and ideally should also afford him comprehensive editing facilities to 'clean up' the data), and 'output' software.

Output software

29. Two examples of output software have already been discussed, namely perspective views with hidden lines removed and shaded pictures. It should be noted that there are

some limitations on the use of these programs - for instance
there is a limit on the amount of data which they can handle
(the exact amount depending on the size of the computer).
Also, in the case of shaded pictures it is often inconven-
ient to obtain a hard copy of the output by photography
direct from the screen as this can entail delays and loss of
accuracy. Some of the limitations on size can be avoided to
some extent by partitioning the data into suitably sized
chunks, and overlaying several pictures to get the end product. There are other techniques for producing hidden-line
pictures, such as the sky-line technique, which are particularly suitable for terrain models and do not suffer from
size limitations as they can read data in a serial form from
a disc file, provided that it has been suitable ordered
first. However, some loss of flexibility is entailed by
this method; it is very difficult to get structures and
buildings added to the model as the algorithm is not a general purpose one.

30. This covers most of the ways of representing surface
models in three dimensions, but of course there are other
more traditional ways which are equally useful in many
fields. Some of these are

> (a) plan of area, with spot heights marked with their
>   level;
> (b) a series of cross-sections;
> (c) feature lines map (this covers the special case of
>   contours), with labelling;
> (d) grid of levels.

These techniques are generally very easy to program, and do
not suffer from serious size limitations. They do not need
special-purpose hardware such as raster-scan displays, and
would provide a quick, cheap means of verifying data and
avoiding expensive errors.

Input software

31. There is little doubt that given the current state of
output technology, the cost-effectiveness of computer visualisation depends to a great extent upon being able to capture
data from a variety of different sources, and convert it to
a relevant form. This has proved to be a continually growing problem; it is found that users become more and more ambitious in their requirements, and are continually coming up
against restrictions imposed by the data generation facilities available.

32. The data required by the perspective viewing programs
would be very laborious to prepare by hand, and there are
several solutions to this problem. The first is based on a
library of standard shapes such as cones, cylinders, boxes
etc., and gives the user a high level language with which he
can assemble these objects into the model he requires, with
the ability to shift, rotate scale, or shear any object.
This greatly simplifies and reduces the data prepared by the
user, and also the input is in an explicit, readable format
and is easy to edit if mistakes are made. The system can
readily be extended by adding new special-purpose primitives
(for instance road signs, lamp standards, bridge abutments
and so on).

33. The second method of data preparation is to work directly from plans and elevations or cross-sections, using a digitiser to obtain coordinate information, possibly allied with
keyboard input for levels. It is also possible to use
stereoscopic pairs of aerial photographs, and to obtain 3-D
coordinate information directly using photogrammetry.

34. Other forms of data handling are required when the information has already been collected in some form (often for
a completely different purpose), and some of these are described below.

DATA PREPARATION

35. The type of data needed in general depends on the sort
of output required; the holding of data in some general purpose format suitable for all outputs would nearly always result in the loss of some information which may be vital in
certain cases, and it will be convenient to deal with the
data preparation by output format.

Perspective output (hidden lines and shaded pictures)

36. In order to obtain perspective views via the general
purpose output programs, the surface has to be represented
as a set of 'tiles', consisting usually of triangles or
quadrilaterals. This information is easiest to generate in
the case of terrain models when the data is held as a series
of heights at regular grid points. In some cases a large
amount of information has been assembled for design and
analysis purposes, and it is possible to convert this very
easily into a form suitable for perspective output. In the
case of BIPS the process is simply to pick up the points on a
cross-section and to join them to corresponding points on

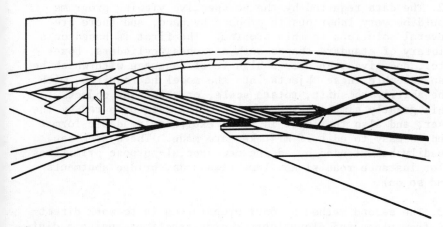

Fig.3. The flexibility of general purpose three-dimensional graphics software is demonstrated here. Data for the road and adjoining earthworks is taken from BIPS, and the building, bridge and road sign are defined manually

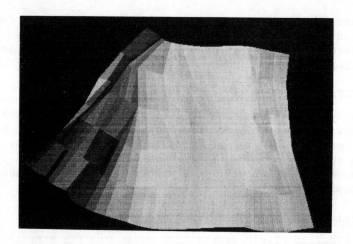

Fig.4. Model generated from digitised input of contours, and output on a raster-scan display

the next cross-section, giving a series of quadrilateral tiles representing the highway and adjoining earthworks (Fig. 3).

37. Software is available to take a series of random spot heights and transform this into heights at given grid points,

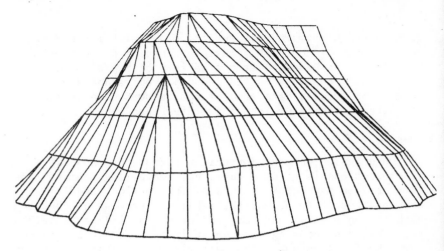

Fig.5. Hidden-lines picture generated from identical data to

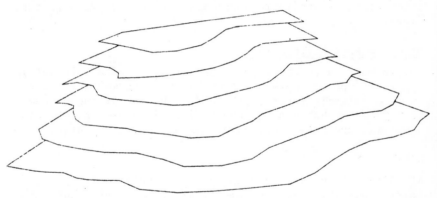

Fig.6. The same modes as Figs 4 and 5, viewed as a series of plane polygons

and this is often a convenient way of modelling the surface. However, when the information is held as a set of feature lines (for example, a set of contours or MOSS data), it is better to try and generate tiles directly. Some work has been done on automatic generation of tiles from digitised input of contours (Figs 4 and 5), although there are many problems in deducing the shape of the implied surface between two contours, particularly at saddle points. Another approach is to simply represent each contour as a plane polygon, and the resulting output represents a series of slices through the model, which can be viewed in perspective (Fig. 6).

Feature lines

38. A straightforward feature-line map (which includes the special case of contours - feature lines at a constant height) can be produced from a variety of different data. For example, contours can be deduced from random spot heights or gridded data, and of course MOSS data is ideal for direct processing into a feature-lines map.

Cross-sections

39. Once again the most convenient format for producing cross-sections is gridded data, but converting feature lines to this form may entail a loss of information, and it is probably better to accept the laborious process of checking each string against each cross-section to find any inter-sections, and deducing the connectivity of these points to form the final output. The ease with which this may be done depends very much on the type of data, and whether or not information is available about the surfaces between feature lines.

Grid and spot height plans

40. In most cases there would be little advantage in obtaining this type of representation if the data was not naturally in a suitable format. The main function of these drawings would probably be to check field data on input to other programs, and here a quick, cheap facility is required.

CONCLUSION

41. Although the use of graphics in ground modelling is fairly restricted at the moment, it seems likely that much greater use will be made of computer drawing facilities as the software is improved.

42. This paper has tried to indicate some areas where current technology may suffice to provide acceptable output for data validation purposes without too much intermediate data processing, and to highlight some of the problem areas in producing perspectives for aesthetic evaluation.

```
:::::::::::::::::::::::::::::::::::::::::::::::::::::::::::::::::::
```
Discussion
```
:::::::::::::::::::::::::::::::::::::::::::::::::::::::::::::::::::
```

PAPERS 1 AND 2

<u>Mr E Malcomson</u> (Computer Services, Northamptonshire County
Council): Paper 2 gives some interesting discussion on the
quandry in which contractors involved in surveying find themselves. They feel they need to automate their procedures
but they suffer from a lack of direction. May I suggest the
reason for this lack of direction is that the client must
specify his requirements. For instance, the client will say
that he requires a computer model to represent the detail
and the level of a particular area. But there is the sug-
gestion that the available techniques are not acceptable in
engineering terms; I refer to Mr Howes' comments on the
degradation of data through the various steps he takes. The
publication of these facts dissuades the client from specifying digital ground models from ground survey methods. This
obviously prolongates the problem of direction.

However, may I report that appropriate techniques are available and, not surprisingly, have been developed by a client
organization. They have been used for more than a year and
several local authorities are utilizing these systems with
great success, especially from the observer's point of view
in the field, where the methods closely follow the traditional approach to data gathering.

<u>Mr J W Wright</u> (President, Land Survey Division, Royal Insti-
tution of Chartered Surveyors): In papers 2 and 3 one author
talks about dealing with a requirement by ground survey and
the other by air survey. Neither of them really gets down
to saying why he does it his way.

In general, the best way to make the map of the ground is by
air survey unless there are reasons against it. One such
reason may be that the area is too small to justify the cost,
which has an irreducible minimum of getting the aeroplane up
in the air and taking photographs from it. One may have
photographs already taken for some other purpose, but these

might be out of date. Another reason may be that the survey
is on too large a scale. There is a limit below which air
survey cannot be used: this is around 1:500. In the UK one
often cannot fly aeroplanes below a certain level in order
to get large scale and one cannot fly them slowly enough to
be able to take photographs without image movement. A third
reason which applies in the UK is that the weather may be
bad and may cause delays.

For something like a reservoir or road survey, where scales
of 1:2500 or so are large enough, and the area is pretty
extensive so that the cost of getting the aircraft up in the
air is justified, then without such restrictions the air survey is liable to win all the time. This is proved very for-
cibly in a film by a leading instrument manufacturer which
shows the speed at which a tachy staff-holder would have to
move to keep up with the operator of a photogrammetric plotting instrument.

Mr Howes in Paper 2 emphasizes the effect of the modern,
automatic-reading field instruments; but these advantages
apply only in a relatively small number of set-ups where a
large number of observations is taken from each set-up. In
such cases the time saved in not having to read the theodolite begins to be important. Working at scale of 1:10 000
or so, the bulk of the time of the surveyor is spent in moving from point to point.

Mr G E Formstone (Midland RCU, Department of Transport):
Mr Howes mentioned that his company collects DGM data by
ground survey and then interpolates levels at the nodes of a
square grid to form the stored model. I should like to make
the point that a more accurate model results if the model is
formed from the surveyed points. Clever surface fitting in
the office cannot reproduce the ground as the surveyor originally saw it.

PAPER 3

Mr J Leatherdale (Mapping Manager, Hunting Surveys Ltd,
Borehamwood): In aerial surveying, the rate of development
is considerable. Two techniques which have been developed
recently may be of interest. First, there is now a fully
automated correlator, producing from a pair of aerial photographs a formidable quantity of digitized heights across the
model by a fully automated process. This is the Gestalt
GPM2, produced in Canada. (Models can be sent there to be
processed.)

The disadvantage of this system at present is that it gives no less than 700 000 recorded points per photo model. The user probably has to spend a considerable amount of computer time editing this down to a usable quantity of data. The other disadvantage is the plot height readings are taken on whatever the photo surface is. If it is the top of trees or buildings, there is no way of distinguishing this. However, the fact remains that a system is available which will produce colossal quantities of data which are then edited down. It may not be too much use in the UK, but with an area of undeveloped tundra or desert where one just wants the natural surface on the photo, this is a formidable tool.

The second system, which is nearer to home in that it is now operating at Hunting Surveys, is to connect a number of conventional stereo plotters not to an off-line recording unit, but on-line to a computer. Although this has been designed primarily to produce data from the plotter and produce a graphical end product, looking more or less like a conventional map, it obviously lends itself to the digital collection of data on magnetic disc and tape and the processing and production of that. In work such as evaluating coal stock volumes and reservoir capacities, the man-hours involved in doing the observing are cut considerably. The quantities of data that can be handled are much greater.

All this, together with Paper 4, points to the fact that capacity is available to produce far too much data and it is becoming increasingly important to assess what patterns of observed data give the accuracy that is required with the maximum efficiency, in order that computer processing may be reduced to a minimum.

<u>Mr P B Jeffreys</u> (Mott, Hay and Anderson, Croydon): For surface modelling for route selection it has been assumed, so far, that one ground model is used at all stages in design, from route selection to final design. This, unfortunately, is not always true.

In developing countries roads or railways of 500-1000 km long are common. If route selection involves choosing a valley through mountains, positioning tunnels and bridges etc., the band of interest could well be 50km wide. Modelling this ground to final design standards would be prohibitively expensive.

Even if expense were no object accurate modelling of this area would be ruled out because the client expects a preliminary design in months.

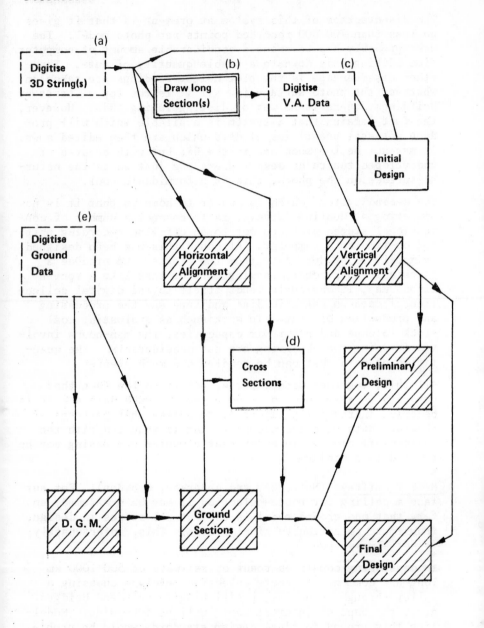

BIPS3

Fig.1

The problem then is to select the optimum route in very
little time working from, typically, 1:50 000 contour maps.
To assist the designer, the facilities in BIPS3 have been
extended. Fig.1 shows, shaded, the normal BIPS3 facilities.
The traditional method, given unlimited time and staff,
would be to draw out lots of ground long section and compare
them. Many vertical alignments would be considered; quantities, bridges, and tunnels for each would be compared.
Finally, after many attempts, a composite alignment would be
decided.

This process has simply been automated by supplementing the
BIPS3 programs. This method allows the engineer to retain
control throughout and data used in any stage of design can
be passed on to later stages.

The maps are inspected and promising routes are drawn on
them. The equipment shown in Fig.2 is a combined digitizer/
plotter used on-line to a large computer. It is used as a
digitizer to take off the map the points of intersection of
the chosen routes and the contours, activity (a) on the diagram. The computer calculates chainages and heights along
each route and a ground long section is drawn - activity (b).

By inspection of these long sections a better guess can be
made at the optimum horizontal alignment and (a) and (b) are
repeated.

This new alignment is probably a composite of several routes

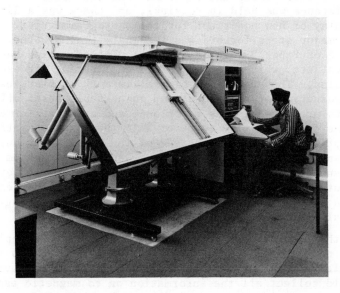

Fig.2

in the same corridor. A vertical alignment can be sketched
on, digitized (c), and passed to the Initial Design program
which will produce bridge and tunnel lengths, quantities etc.
The vertical alignment can be modified as necessary and the
program re-run.

The optimized alignments, digitized at (a) and (c), can then
be passed to the standard BIPS3 programs. If the original
routes in this corridor were chosen with care they, combined,
will produce a fair model of the ground. These are passed
to a new program (d) which, with the horizontal alignment
output, will produce BIPS3 cross-section data.

This, with the vertical alignment, can be processed in the
Preliminary Design program to give better quantities than
the initial design as it takes side slopes into account. As
the design proceeds to larger scale maps two further digi-
tizing techniques, (e) on the diagram, can be used to give
more accuracy.

Dr J P Stott (Transport and Road Research Laboratory,
Crowthorne), Session Chairman: Mr Cheffins, would you
like to say something about progress in the next few
years?

Mr O W Cheffins, presenter of Paper 3 (Assistant Mapping
Manager (Technical), Fairey Surveys Ltd, Maidenhead): Recently the four-yearly International Photogrammetric Society
conference was held in Helsinki, and there was a dazzling
display of new equipment for the photogrammetrist. One of
the major steps forward was the analytical plotter. Figs 3
and 5 of Paper 3 show an analogue plotter, which has pulleys,
wires, etc. which are subject to engineering stresses and
strains. The analytical plotter is much simpler, using a
reproduction of the photograph on a stable base: all measurements are taken in the x-y plane, and are transformed by
means of a real-time computer into the correct spatial res-
titution dimensions. Instead of the model being built up by
an analogue, it is built up by an analytical system. The
orientation of photogrammetric models which take between 20
minutes and an hour or two in an analogue plotter can be done
in a couple of minutes by an unskilled person using an analytical plotter.

At the Helsinki conference, mention was made of replacing
the camera: instead of having a camera with a lens and film
emulsion, you would have an electronic scanning device which
could collect all the information on to magnetic tape or

disc. Really, I think that is going too far, even if we consider beyond the year 2000. The time is a long way off when the film camera will be replaced. If the electronics had been invented first, what a marvellous step forward we would have seen in the film camera!

Mr Leatherdale referred to automatic correlators for scanning stereoscopic models but electronic rastors cannot yet differentiate between houses and haystacks. We are analogues ourselves. We do not want to be daleks. It is a good thing that we should stay as we are for the foreseeable future and that the capital investment which has been made in analogue devices is given a few more years of useful life.

Mr Wright: There are one or two further points which are of interest on the question of air survey versus ground survey. A good reason for not using air surveys is if the whole ground is covered by trees, because all one would get would be a map of the top of the trees. The Directorate of Overseas Surveys had an example of this in an overseas country. Away from the coast the ground is largely covered by trees. A Canadian company has made 1:50 000 maps of the whole of the backland. DOS has been mapping the cultivated coastal plain and has now been asked to consider producing better maps of the interior. We have said that the existing maps with 50 or 100 ft contours are as good as one can expect unless the trees are cleared, to which of course the answer has come: 'How do we know which areas to clear without better maps?' This is a case where if one wants to have a larger scale, more accurately contoured survey of the ground, one has to send in parties with levels among the trees to produce it.

Another factor in the choice between air and ground survey is the density of population. (There are two things land surveyors dislike: trees and people. A third, when they get into really refined work, is the atmosphere - which is why the moon would be ideal for survey!) When surveying an area with many buildings, trees, houses and people, one gets objections and queries; and it is easier to do the detail survey from the air, so as to have as little survey work done on the ground as possible. An important advantage of air survey is that in addition to the line maps which the photogrammetrist produces, one gets the photographs themselves. Although it is a disadvantage for the photogrammetrist to take the photographs at a relatively large scale (e.g. 1:40 000 for 1:50 000 mapping), the DOS has done this because other people want to use them. The early DOS maps were uncon-

toured but with the positions of the photographs shown.
Other technical people, like geologists, foresters and surveyors, could use the photographs and the maps and did not
have to locate or map the features they identified. They
could interpret what they were seeing and locate and map the
features from the DOS maps and air photo positions.

A ground surveyor is required to get the names of the features; air survey cannot do that.

Another difference is the kind of error. All surveys have
errors. The question is whether these are acceptable or not.
The basic difference, I believe, between the ground surveyor
and the aerial surveyor is that if he is working to the
limits, the ground surveyor often has difficulty in locating
himself but knows his height; while the photogrammetrist
knows exactly where he is because once the four corners of
his overlap are controlled he moves absolutely accurately
anywhere within the framework, but he does not always know
what height he is getting particularly if he has been trying
to squeeze out the last foot or two. Mr Cheffins could elaborate the reasons for this; awful things do happen in aerial
cameras. The emulsion sometimes moves and the commonest
fault usually is that the film is not flat. In this system
for producing spot heights to 1:5000 of the flying height
one is dealing in very small distances on the photographs –
of the order of 10 µm.

When I was in Hunting Surveys we had an example of this
where parts of a large-scale map in Malaysia were made by us
from air photographs and the rest by a local RE ground survey. At the joins discrepancies of three times the 2 ft
contour interval were found. Tests showed that the air survey, because of grass and thin bush, had errors up to 2 ft
in height; the rest, I believe, was due to errors in position of the ground survey which was not easy under the trees.

Mr Cheffins: All I should like to say about film flattening
is that it used to be a problem but modern cameras when properly maintained rarely give trouble.

PAPER 4

Mr Formstone: I should like to speak about the triangle digital ground model which is the least known of those already
spoken about. The method of data collection which is most
suitable for the triangle DGM is ground survey, but data can
also be collected from contoured maps by digitizer or less

satisfactorily by direct scaling. The collection of data
from air photographs has not yet been attempted.

No matter which DGM is chosen, the problem of which points
shall be selected to represent the terrain must be solved.
With the square grid, the problem is solved once the grid
spacing is decided. With the string DGM, although the selection of points does take the trend of the surface into
account, only the relationship between points in the string
is recorded; the relationship with points in other strings
is not recorded. An advantage of the triangle DGM over all
others is that the relationship of a point with others around
it is recorded and, therefore, the extraction of information
from the model is considerably assisted. It is true that
the recording of the point connections can be demanding on
time but it is thought that the effort is worthwhile.

How does the surveyor select his triangle DGM points? Having
fixed two points, that are either on a terrain break line or
approximately on a contour, such that the ground gradient
between them is fairly uniform, the surveyor looks for a
third point to complete the triangle. The ground gradient
between each of the original points and the third point must
not depart from the straight line drawn between the points
by more than a specified amount. If one is extracting data
from contoured maps, it is fairly easy to see where the
changes in gradient and curvature occur.

Data is retrieved from a triangle DGM by sequential access
methods. The points at which each cross-section cuts the
sides of each triangle are found by linear interpolation. A
cross-section with ten points on it will cost about 10p to
create.

Mr G S Craine (Management Services Engineer, Durham County
Council): I should like to mention research carried out at
Durham County Council and within the road construction sub-
unit into the accuracy of surface models as stored within
the MOSS system. Our research appears complementary to that
of Drs Stott and Grist but approaches the problem from a
different aspect.

MOSS is a surface modelling system for recording many types
of land form such as existing ground, quarries, stockpiles
and new works. Such modelling must be to a required accuracy; ground and aerial survey techniques have been developed with this accuracy in mind and have been supported with
considerable field research.

We are concerned with string models from either aerial or

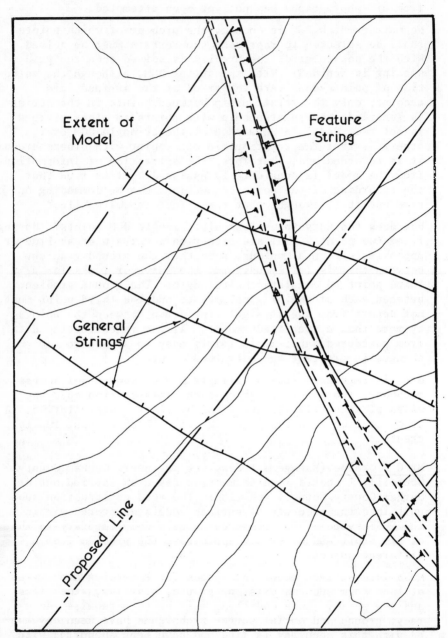

Fig.3. Typical test area

ground survey and their content consists primarily of 3D strings defining all angular features, supported by further general strings to depict ground curvature. In the case of aerial survey these are contour strings and for ground survey they are further 3D strings. The saturation provided by the general strings is dependent on the scale and accuracy required.

The research into the accuracy of these models has taken the form of an investigation of the various sources of error, which were identified as

    (a) quality of model error
        (i) model content
        (ii) interpolation methods
    (b) survey error
        (i) systematic
        (ii) random.

This work[1-3] has led to the preparation of a method specification for string models which is being used throughout the UK. Further, we are carrying out field tests on all ground models prepared from this specification and the ultimate aim is to provide a test specification for future contracts.

The field test method (Fig.3) consists of sampling the model by taking sections within selected test areas located at regular intervals throughout the model. Each area will have three general sections across the model plus a section along a selected feature. These sections are recorded with points at every 10 m and at every angular change of grade.

Equivalent model sections are extracted for each of the field sections which are statistically compared to determine the mean vertical difference and confidence intervals. In the case of the selected features the horizontal error can be similarly determined.

The technique is best illustrated with examples from an actual field test and the results are presented as shown in Fig.4. The original contract specification requested that 85% of the results were within a specified interval and the diagram indicates for each section the mean error and its 85% confidence interval. The results prove the acceptability of the model and the practicability of the technique.[4]

Independently of recording models of existing ground, MOSS provides model design facilities which to date have been used mainly for highway design, especially in complex interchange situations. Earthworks volumes determined from such models have been proven to accuracies of 1-3% and confirm the suitability of this surface modelling approach.

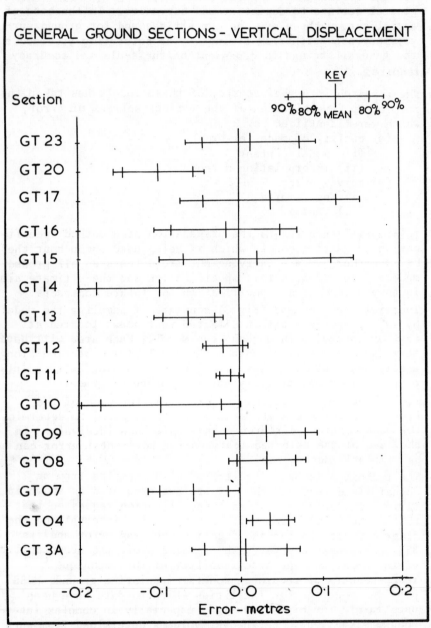

Fig.4. Presentation of results

Mr J Houlton (West Sussex County Council, MOSS Consortium):
The MOSS Consortium (involving the county councils of Durham,
Northamptonshire and West Sussex) has been involved for the
last five years on the development of the string system of
ground modelling or surface modelling. This has been done
in conjunction with air and ground survey contractors and
has resulted in a viable and economic method of surface
modelling with the minimum of interpolation associated with
it. In addition, extensive research and development has
been undertaken to test the hypotheses forming the basis of
the system. Much of the work has been incorporated in the
Transport and Road Research Laboratory work on the Wensleydale project. Recently, work has been done on the development of a method for testing ground models - a very significant factor when one considers the promotion of a method of
surface modelling. The method has been widely accepted in
Australia, and is in use in the Netherlands and in Turkey.

The word MOSS has been used many times at this Conference
(cf. Paper 1 (§§3 and 16), Paper 4 (§13) and Mr Craine's con-
tribution to the discussion) and there are examples in the
papers of the Conference of drawings produced by the MOSS
system. MOSS is a computer system, the first to be evolved
specifically for surface modelling. It solves a class of
problems which can be defined as the interaction of three-
dimensional surfaces and pieces of three-dimensional geometry. It can be applied not only to highway design but to
many other fields - the modelling of ground surfaces and road
surfaces, detailed models for surveying and restructuring of
Ordnance Survey digital maps.

Mr M G Derrington (Manchester University): I should like to
report some work which has been done at Manchester University on calculating volumes. The investigation was in three
parts, all carried out on rectangular areas with the data in
the form of a rectangular grid of surface levels. The basis
of the work was the belief that increasing the number of
levels should improve accuracy and that in rough terrain
more heights are needed to achieve a given accuracy than in
smooth terrain.

The first application was to mathematically generated surfaces. The co-ordinate values in all three directions were
therefore defined, also the exact volume to be measured. We
were trying to find the best formula for calculating volume.
Three sorts were tried - polynomials put end to end, overlapping polynomials and splines. Splines are polynomials
put end to end but with slope and curvature made continuous

at the junctions. The results of these investigations were
partly vitiated by the fact that when data was densified to
improve accuracy, round-off errors in the computer rapidly
became more important than errors in calculation. They led
to the choice of six formulae with differing advantages.

Some experiments were carried out on natural surfaces obtained by aerial photography of both flat and hilly regions.
The digital ground models were obtained to 0.1 m at 5 m
intervals and the true volume was taken to be the mean of
all calculated volumes since no one method of calculation
converged uniformly on a fixed value.

In each area, samples of data were taken to investigate what
was meant by 'roughness' of terrain and to see how many
heights were needed, in that area, to calculate the volume
to a specified accuracy. Some of the factors thought likely
to be associated with roughness were steepness of slope, number of changes of slope and range of height. The sample
consisted of two lines of heights in each direction, parallel to the sides. Fourier series were fitted to the sample
heights and certain derived coefficients were chosen as in-
dicators of roughness. Roughness coefficients, different in
the two directions, were correlated with accuracies of volume estimation so that from them the total number of heights
required to achieve volume estimation accuracies of 1%, 2%,
5% etc. could be estimated. This minimum number required
was associated with an oblong rectangular grid of heights
which, for convenience of survey, was related by a further
series of experiments to a square grid giving the same
accuracy.

I should like to mention three points which can upset com-
parative studies. First, relative accuracies are very dependent on net volume if cut and fill exist. Second, bulking
and consolidation of cut and fill cannot be taken into
account in a generalized study. Third, on strictly logical
grounds, a terrain roughness coefficient used for volume computation is a function of the height variation in a length,
not in unit length. It follows from the last point that the
same number of heights should be taken in a cross-section as
are taken in a longitudinal section if the roughnesses in
the two directions are the same. Present practice is very
different from this and can only be justified by the engineers' need to calculate volume distribution in order to
measure haulage as well as to calculate a volume balance.

In the controversy about land survey, most people would
allow that one cannot beat land survey for the accuracy one

gets for relative heights in the immediate neighbourhood of
the instrument station. If roads could be designed relative
to approximately known stations along the route instead of
to an absolute datum, some savings in survey costs might be
made.

PAPER 5

<u>Mr J R Hollwey</u> (Past President, Land Survey Section, Royal
Institution of Chartered Surveyors): Commander Glen refers
to the production of co-tidal charts as being a computer
activity. I wonder whether he would say a little more about
the possibilities of adding further information to these
charts for an immediate response from people approaching har-
bours. Does he envisage a future situation in which, let us
say, a tanker captain coming up the English Channel could
'dial up' Taunton and get not only an input on to a video
screen which would tell him the·pattern of the sea in the
approaches to the port of London, but possibly also some
meteorological input as well?

<u>Commander Glen</u>: Obviously, there is a considerable meteoro-
logical element in all tidal observations. Firstly, the sea
acts as an inverse barometer. Also it is affected by the
wind. We therefore get many non-tidal effects in our observations. We analyse to remove these effects, which are
assumed to be random and not predictable. However, we are
bound to get a certain number of these effects remaining in
the harmonic constants which are the results of our analysis.
Thus we end up with a very noisy picture of the tidal movements. To show just how noisy - when observing from oil
rigs in the middle of the North Sea, we were looking for a
2 m signal among 10 m background noise. That is why we do
not get extremely accurate results. Therefore, much of the
drawing of the charts has been an attempt to represent the
tidal movements from data which also contains a large element of meteorological effects.

The situation regarding data for tankers and their arrival
at ports is in the process of development. We have an experimental 'negative surge warning system'. A surge is
defined as occuring when the actual level of the sea is different from that predicted. Normally, it is described as a
surge when a positive surge is meant; i.e., the actual level
is higher than predicted. A 'negative surge' occurs when
the actual level is lower than predicted; an effect which
might, in extreme circumstances, cause a tanker to run into

danger. We therefore have a system at the Meteorological Office, Bracknell, which is doing its best to warn tankers and other large ships when the level of the sea is expected to be lower than predicted.

At present we are only able to do this over a very restricted area in the southern North Sea and it does not always work. We do not issue warnings for surges less than 1 m. The system is still very much on an experimental basis with research continuing to enable improvements to be made.

Mr R J Bridle (Chief Highway Engineer, Department of the Environment), Session Chairman: The practice is obviously considerably more complicated than the basic underlying theory. An interesting point is the amount of variation caused merely because of the shape of the coastline. A narrow estuary presumably has a great effect on the prediction; and the utility of being able to predict not only the level of the surface but the forces which might be imparted by the water seems to be very important, particularly in the case of oil rigs and structures below the surface of the sea such as catenary tunnels'.

Commander Glen: I have left out many of the details in order to concentrate on the basic principles. I have assumed that the moon is in a circular orbit. Obviously this is not so; the orbit is elliptical and the moon goes round it at a varying speed. Thus numerous corrections have to be added to the basic principles. Then, in shallow water, there is distortion of the basic sine curve. Here we need to use higher harmonics to obtain an efficient prediction. In a modern prediction for a port like Southend, these are always included.

Mr Bridle: Would modelling the floor of the Channel help towards refining the prediction?

Commander Glen: Models have been made; so far they have not provided predictions which are as effective as those based on the analysis of observations. That is not to say that they will not be as good one day.

Mr Bridle: Could you use the observations to calibrate the models?

Commander Glen: This is done, but it is extremely difficult to make a model sufficiently sensitive to record all the undulations of the sea bed.

Mr Derrington: Could this information be used with sea bed contours to predict total curves?

Commander Glen: The difficulty is that in practice horizontal movements of the sea are much more sensitive than vertical movements to meteorological effects. One result of this is that we have not yet got a model which enables us to predict tidal streams really accurately. However, progress in this field is being made.

Dr Stott: Having measured what happens at specific points, is there any way thereafter of accounting for why it happened? Also, perhaps Commander Glen would comment on methods of interpolation.

If errors occur, I wonder what the warning can be, and what proportion of the total tidal rise the inaccuracy would be.

Mr Bridle: Also, it may be interesting to know the reasons for differences in accuracy in different places: that might indicate the contributions of various parameters.

Commander Glen: Interpolation is done as best we can, depending on the data. One of the problems is that the data are not uniform in their standards. Therefore, one has to look at each individual set of data when it is plotted on the rough sheet, assess its value and then decide how to interpolate between that and neighbouring data. Great care is taken with this interpolation as there are numerous possible sources of innaccuracy in the data.

Next one takes into account the fact that we are dealing with the movement of millions of tons of water. It is therefore not possible for this mass to suddenly change direction or stop. On this basis the contours of the tidal movement are drawn by an experienced draughtsman.

When I mentioned the accuracy of tidal surge predictions, I said there was an alternative method. This is for the harbour master to watch his tide gauge, compare it with the prediction and advise the approaching ship by radio if conditions are unsuitable. That is a very basic way of passing the information which is always available. In fact it is part of the system used by the Storm Tide Warning Service. They have recorders at Bracknell which are connected to tide gauges as far north as Wick and as far south as Southend. By using these and some mathematical formulae, they predict the progression of the surge down the coast and then keep

check on its progress. By this means they are able to provide a service which is reasonably effective, though in need
of improvement.

As to the magnitude of error in tidal predictions, that is a
very sensitive subject. There have been suggestions that
all countries should publish information concerning the standard of their predictions. I have always been against that
on principle because so much depends on the weather conditions. Countries with stable weather will always appear to
be providing much better predictions than those, such as the
UK, where the weather is extremely variable, not only from
day to day but also from year to year. If we take a 'standard port' like Devonport - all results from standard ports
in the UK are about the same - where we are using the best
available techniques, the standard deviation of the differences between predicted and observed heights is about 0.2 m.
In an area with much more stable weather such as Honolulu,
the standard deviation is about 0.1 m. As we are considering about 700 occurrences each year, we must expect surges
as great as three standard deviations about ten times a year
on average. Positive surges of 3 m and negative surges of
2 m have been recorded.

PAPER 6

Mr Cratchley: It is interesting to follow Commander Glen.
There are some similarities, although it might appear unlikely on the face of it, between the sort of work that we have
been doing and that with which he is concerned. These similarities really relate to the uncertainty and complex nature
of the data involved. By contrast with some of the other
Conference papers, in considering a geological situation we
are concerned not with just one surface but with a number of
surfaces at different depths in the earth. We are also concerned with the properties and behaviour of the materials
which make up the various deposits between these bounding
surfaces.

I should like to develop this theme by describing in outline
our work in South Essex in connection with the previously
mooted third London airport at Maplin. This regional survey
had two main objectives. The first was to provide planners
with geological criteria to aid in their planning for the
development of the hinterland to any airport development.
The second, while recognizing that detailed site investigation will always be required for specific developments, was

to give a guide to the most economic way of carrying out
these investigations and to methods of testing and so on.
At the outset, we decided to put all the information on to a
fairly complex computer-based data bank. There were several
objectives in deciding to go for a computer bank, discussed
in detail in the paper. An important aspect was the experimental nature of the survey. Geological information has
traditionally been presented in terms of stratigraphic units.
For example, a geological map shows the rock types occurring
at the ground surface in terms of their age, origin and, to
a lesser extent, their lithology. We wanted to experiment
with a presentation in which the engineering and physical
characteristics of the rocks could be portrayed. Computer
graphics appeared to give a fairly flexible way of attempting to do this by producing experimental maps and so on at
working stages. We also wished to carry out statistical
analyses on the geotechnical parameters determined for the
various units in the area. These helped in classifying the
materials geotechnically; one wants to group together materials of like engineering behaviour and physical character.
One method is by multivariate or cluster analysis. A computer bank enabled this to be done more rapidly.

The computer data bank has nine files of information, so
that it is fairly complex and involves a number of different
computing facilities (Fig.5). These enable us to answer
straightforward queries about ground conditions, such as the
geotechnical parameters in a certain locality, or the borehole logs and test results from the nearest boreholes to
that locality. We can produce a variety of maps of surfaces
and thicknesses of geological formations, together with sections, tables of properties etc.

One of the most important aspects of the geology of the area
is the presence of the compressible silty clays and sands of
the Recent Alluvium, which overlie basal gravel and the undulating London Clay surface particularly in the east of the
area. One of the computer outputs is a perspective view,
from the east, of the London Clay surface in South Essex
(Fig.6). This shows the outline of the Essex coast, Foulness
Island and the rivers Crouch and Roach. The present Crouch
Estuary has a buried channel and there is an older channel
around Rochford. Both are filled with soft materials and
sandy gravel and therefore would have to be taken into account in planning, particularly for tunnels or bridges at
major crossings of access routes. The form and depths of
this surface of London Clay are therefore important in engineering planning and it is useful to compare the surface

Discussion

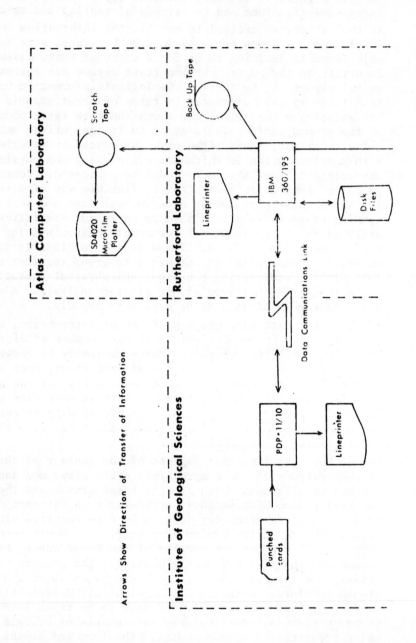

Arrows Show Direction of Transfer of Information

Institute of Geological Sciences

Atlas Computer Laboratory

Rutherford Laboratory

Scratch Tape

SD4020 Microfilm Plotter

Back Up Tape

IBM 360/195

Lineprinter

Disk Files

Data Communications Link

PDP-11/10

Lineprinter

Punched Cards

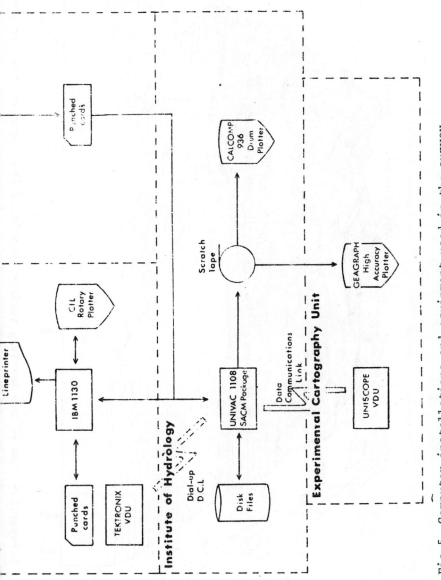

Fig.5. Computer installations and equipment used in the survey

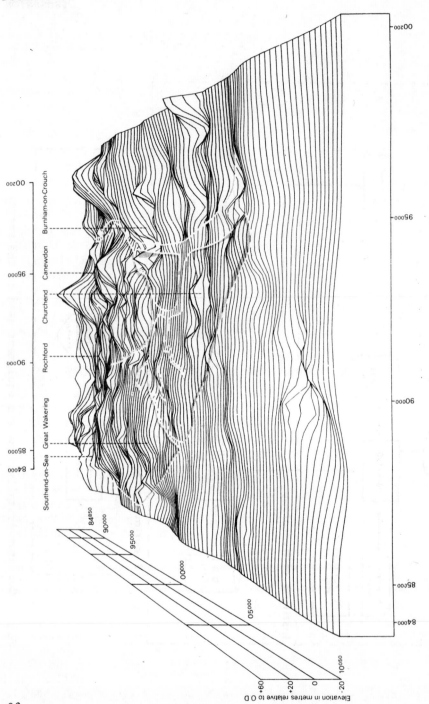

Fig.6. Perspective view of the Tertiary surface from Foulness to Hockley from the east

model from a computer system with that obtained from a geologist's contour plot based on the same data (Figs 7 and 8). The differences in the two models arise partly because of the lack of data and of our knowledge about the form of the surface (a typical 'terrain line' cannot be approximated until a second or even third stage of borehole and possibly geophysical investigation), and because the geologist compensates for this lack of data by drawing the contours to fit his interpretation of how that surface was produced. The manual plot (Fig.7) therefore shows buried river channels while the computer plot (Fig.8) tends to show closures and a more rounded contour pattern.

In relation to obtaining a good model of the geology, I cannot answer the question of costs specifically. There will be a point beyond which, for economic reasons, one cannot go; it will just be too costly to get more data. One therefore faces the dilemma of attempting to define the minimum number of data points required to define all the surfaces in an area. This cannot be done at the outset because the surfaces are not known. Modelling of geological surfaces (particularly complex ones at shallow depths) is a long way behind the modelling of visible surfaces.

PAPER 7

Mr H Cowling (Organizing Committee): In surface modelling the mathematical techniques and the accuracy of the computer procedures tend mainly to be considered. This emphasis must not be without regard to the engineering and design requirements of the processes in which they are used.

For instance, the projects Mr Whitton has described, while primarily designed for the architect's requirements, will often also be used to calculate quantities; the land surveyor, the landscape architect and the quantity surveyor are all likely to show an interest in the output. Quantities will be measured in accordance with the Standard Method of Measurement by the quantity surveyor, and any accuracy greater than that required by the method, and furnished by elaboration of the computer procedures, or requirements for additional data, will be of doubtful value.

Mr Whitton: This goes back to what I said previously about redundant information. We are now moving into a specialist field, talking about large buildings, and it is the accuracy of the information and the volume of the information which only one person working there needs. In the past, people

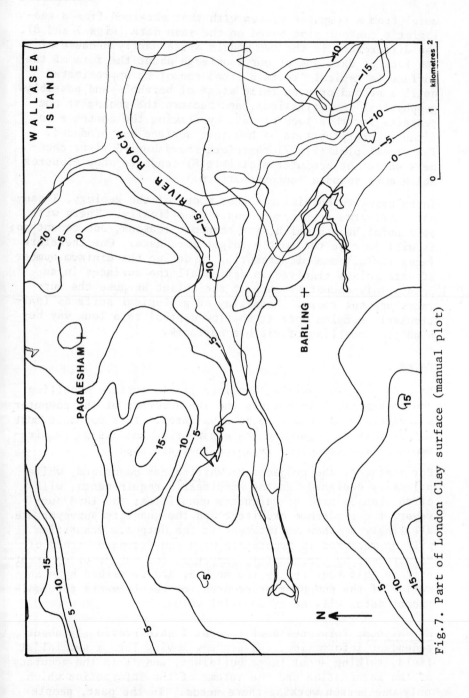

Fig.7. Part of London Clay surface (manual plot)

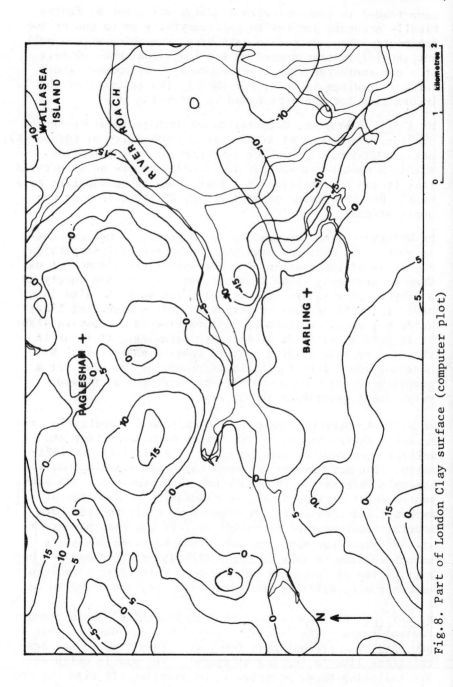

Fig.8. Part of London Clay surface (computer plot)

have tended to come out with drawings which may be fantastically accurate and try to get everything on to one or two documents. Now, we need a data base from which we can pull out the information needed by the individual who requests it - not smothered with other comments. My comment about lots of drawings is true, but that is the accuracy of the information for the person who is receiving it.

Mr A Bijl (Director, Computer Aided Architectural Design Studies, Department of Architecture, University of Edinburgh), Session Chairman: A problem in representing information within a machine is whether information can be so structured that it can be extracted in a form which is appropriate to a user. Has this issue cropped up, Mr Whitton, in your own applications?

Mr Whitton: It has cropped up as an issue. I believe that in your field when you have put data codes against particular items of information, you are working in advance of us. When we are doing these drawings, we specify them purely as a symbol, as a square or rectangle, and vary the size in order to build up what is basically just a number of lines. We do not actually store the information as a concrete slab. It is just a system of lines in the drawing. It is up to the user of that drawing just to specify what it is. We have not moved into the field of measuring the slab for a quantity surveyor or a contractor; we do not at present worry about quantities in any way.

Mr Bijl: Architects commonly find extreme difficulty in expressing their concerns - the issues with which they are working when dealing with buildings - explicitly and logically. You may have experienced this when planning how to assemble information in a machine. Problems which are presented exist outside of any consideration of machines or mathematical techniques; problems may originate from more general consideration of buildings. In the last paragraph of your paper you make the point that building designers have been slow to take up these techniques: this may not be a criticism of designers but may be a pointer to some inherent characteristics of the task which they are asked to do.

Mr Whitton: Architects tend to describe buildings in psychological terms - the 'comfort factor' was one measure that I saw used by a psychologist for this. They tend to use descriptions like 'a feeling of space'. The way in which we are tailoring these programs is by starting off with the con-

crete and steel and moving towards the architect very slowly,
so that he can see how the other professions can use the
machine and perhaps, in 10-15 years, he may be quite happy
to use it himself. For the present, I think, architects perhaps need to be protected from the machine, because it can
be confusing. As you said, they can put in data too, but if
the process cannot be dealt with manually people will get
completely out of their depth if they try using machines to
do it.

Mr Wright: Architects are emotional artists as well as engineers and no doubt they sometimes find it difficult to define
the principles of their designs. Engineers are used to line
maps but one tends to forget that many of the features shown
on a map, especially types of vegetation or land use, are
the result of judgements by the cartographers who put items
seen on the air photographs into specific categories shown
in the legend. Sometimes the judgements are wrong.

Digital records also require the conversion of what may be
more uncertain data into a formal series of categories.
With a topographical map much of the data, such as contours,
are precise; but with thematic maps the interpretation by
geologists or soil surveyors is less certain; this is shown
by discrepancies at sheet edges of their draft maps which
have to be removed when they are fair drawn. Similar effects
may occur in records like confidential reports where characteristics like energy, dedication, reliability and initia-
tive have to be quantified, sometimes with an apparent precision of detail out of all proportion to the probable accuracy of the report.

The advantages of putting data in digital form are that it
forces the authors of it to make up their minds; the danger
is that the results are tidier and apparently more precise
than they really are, and may give them an authority which
the data do not justify.

Mr Cowling: It is in my view essential to ensure that for
each practical application the appropriate type of terrain
model, mathematical techniques, and data requirements should
be selected by consideration of each stage of the calculation process.

Regarding Mr Whitton's presentation, I wonder whether he is
not looking too much at the tail-end of the total process,
the drawing work, rather than the earlier computation. My
experience has been in the development of some of the large

road design systems to which he has referred; the first jus-
tification for these came from the obviation of the time-
consuming calculation of quantities. Automatic drawing of
the results gave a far lower return on cost than the calculation of quantities.

There was also another value from the use of computer calculation. Mr Austin of Freeman Fox said at a previous discussion that the tedium of drawing cross-sections at 100 ft
intervals for the 25 mile length of the M5 had tended to
strip his drawing office of young engineers. They found
more interesting jobs elsewhere! There was an immediate
trade-in from going over to computers for the calculations.

Might it not be worth while to look back into the calculation processes, to see whether there might be earlier computation stages, beside the final design presentation, which
can be sold to the architect?

Mr Whitton: Those comments are very interesting. The problem is that we have never found that the architect does
many calculations in the mathematical sense. He is interested in interpersonal relationships, the people who will use
the building, the means of communication within the building
and the atmosphere within the building. Obviously, there
are the physical problems - the thing must be kept water-
tight and it must stand up - but they are the structural
engineer's problems or the problems of the services engineers.

Going back to the previous comment, design is a cyclic process and the architect may not be able to make up his mind
until he has seen the drawing and judged what will actually
happen. Then, it is not a question of calculation but of
his decision on a number of priorities which can only be defined in non-mathematical terms. He will look at the drawing and say: 'That will not work. From my experience, I
know that people do not like that kind of entrance hall or
staircase.' That is really why we are aiming at this end of
the production process. We can produce the drawings, the
calculations can be done separately by the structural engineer, and the engineers and architects can then discuss what
the final product is. It can either be accepted or, if we
go back around the design cycle, we can make a change and
rapidly calculate its effect on the engineering side of the
design process, and the architect can pick a situation and
go on to the next point on the design programme.

PAPER 8

Mr Hollwey: I take it that all the surfaces that you are using are plane surfaces and not curved in any way?

Mr P Dirdal, presenter of Paper 8 (Computer Aided Design Centre, Cambridge): The surfaces used are made up from quadrilaterals.

Mr Hollwey: You have not yet moved into the field of trying to put one behind another?

Mr Dirdal: We can manipulate the shading in order to make curved surfaces look smooth.

Mr Bijl, Session Chairman: Could you explain the distinction between information describing roads and embankments and further information which you need in order to generate the display of buildings, lamp posts and so on: does every new image require new input to describe the environment in which a road is being modelled?

Mr Dirdal: Once the structure, or assembly of structures, is modelled, we do not need to add any further data. If one wants to produce some form of movie, there will be programs which automatically generate what we call the viewing parameters of the basic data required to get proper perspectives. All one need give the computer is the path along which one wants to move.

Mr Bijl: The purpose of the examples which you showed is primarily directed at visualization of forms, which might impinge on some other activity such as engineering - perhaps a road alignment or a bridge construction. Is this a fair general comment? Are there any problems as to whether the resources which are necessary to achieve this standard of visualization are appropriate?

Mr Dirdal: No, all the techniques are generally applicable to any application, whether architectural or engineering. The reason that there are so many road and bridge construction applications is that this is a discipline which seems to be rather more receptive to this type of technique. There is a great demand on the engineering side to produce evidence of what the structure or the scheme would look like. Examples are the BIPS suite or the MOSS suite; e.g., where the DGM exists, data can be input straight into a visualization facility without any further data preparation. If one wanted to add further details to the models (e.g., bridges, lamp posts or houses) this is readily done using the library of predefined primitives. The additional time involved in producing these details would be the time it takes to produce the additional data; the road data would already exist.

Mr Bijl: Do you have information on what it is that people actually look at when they are presented with such a visualization? Do they gain an overall subjective impression or is there some more specific purpose?

Mr Dirdal: There is no way that I can answer that.

Mr Wright: One of the restrictions on the introduction of these techniques in the design office is the cost and availability of the hardware. I wonder whether Mr Dirdal has any comments on the future availability of hardware so that more engineers could have their own personal screens or plotters for use as and when required.

Mr Dirdal: The most important thing is that the cost of hardware keeps dropping. Also, the technology of micro-processors makes it possible to build hardware which can be used in conjunction with cheap plotters. These could be stationed in the drawing office and linked over an ordinary telephone line to some central computer. I certainly see the opportunities presenting themselves through the advancement of this technology. Whether displays would be linked to a micro-processor too, or whether it could be afforded in local government to acquire one per drawing office or design office, I do not know - but certainly the same principles would apply. It would be possible to build micro-processors which are very cheap, and to program these to drive displays which would be used to view and interact with data as it is held or processed in the main computer.

Mr Bijl: I think that hardware is reducing in cost. Software seems to be increasing in cost - both in development and maintenance - to users. It looks as if this trend will continue, particularly as people become more demanding and ambitious.

Brigadier E P J Williams (Ferranti Ltd): The cost of data collection for input is relatively high and if that data is to be used for only one specific purpose the economics of an

automated system come into question. The essential requirement is to create a data base which can be used by a number
of users. There must be human intervention, because much of
the work we do, whether design or mapping or anything else,
is totally illogical - and the computer cannot compete with
that. Also, the reason for the increasing cost of software
is the number of different systems to be maintained, and
the only way to solve that problem is through systems which
create a central data bank of information.

REFERENCES

1. Craine G S and Heatherington S (Planning and Transport
   Research and Computation Co. (ed.)). The accuracy of
   digital ground models. In Surface and subsurface survey
   and mapping. PTRC, London, 1973.

2. Heatherington S and Craine G S (Planning and Transport
   Research and Computation Co. (ed.)). Aerial surveyed
   string digital ground models. In Road design 2 (special-
   ized topic): proceedings of summer annual meeting, 1974.
   PTRC, London, 1974.

3. Heatherington S. An assessment of aerial surveyed string
   digital ground models. MSc thesis, University of Durham,
   1974.

4. Department of the Environment, North Eastern Road Construction Unit, Durham Sub-Unit. A19 Billingham diver-
   sion - ground model accuracy report. NERCU, Durham Sub-
   Unit, 1976.

:::

Closing address

:::

J R Hollwey (Past President of the Land Survey Section of the Royal Institution of Chartered Surveyors)

I feel at the end of this Conference that there are many problems still unsolved. We are only at the beginning of this activity, rather than the end.

Perhaps the most fundamental problem is the question of data input. It is, I believe, axiomatic in many activities with a computer that if you put garbage in, you will get garbage out. We are not yet sure about the distribution of our input data - where to locate it, even how to gather it. It may be that each individual problem has a different solution whereas we are always seeking a general solution.

The second problem which remains, in my mind, is the question of reliability of results. Probably the only way of knowing with absolute certainty that one's answer is the right one is to take a great mass of sand, measure it photogrammetrically, and put it through a sieve and count how many grains there are. The reliability tests have the veneer - I apologize for that word - of respectability, but they are expressed in standard deviations and such things, which do not necessarily give a measure of the departure from truth.

The nature of the surface being dealt with is another major problem. This came out in Commander Glen's paper and in Mr Cratchley's paper on engineering geology. The problem of the fissures in clay alone means that the mathematical surface must be very suspect. One must be a geologist to have a feel for the material underlying the surface which at this moment the computer does not have. Perhaps this could be built in, and perhaps, also, the co-tidal surface, the surface of London Clay, or a surface of Mendip limestone could be expressed in a mathematical form, but I shudder to think what the expression might be like.

The concept of multi-purpose systems for buildings with

Closing address

total graphics facilities again raises the problem of input and output and definition. A comment made by Mr Williams from Ferranti is that we must seek all the time for reliable basic data banks and seek to extract from those banks the information that we want in trying to provide the information that the client wants in the bank to start with. It is a hard problem and one that has certainly not been solved.